Farm waggons and carts

James Arnold

David & Charles

Newton Abbot · London · North Pomfret (VT) · Vancouver

To Raphael A. Salaman

ISBN   0 7153 7330 7
Library of Congress Catalog Card Number 76-54081

Set in 10pt on 12pt Times New Roman
and printed in Great Britain
by Redwood Burn Limited, Trowbridge & Esher
for David & Charles (Publishers) Limited
Brunel House   Newton Abbot   Devon

Published in the United States of America
by David & Charles Inc
North Pomfret   Vermont 05053   USA

Published in Canada
by Douglas David & Charles Limited
1875 Welch Street   North Vancouver   BC

Contents

Introduction

One realises with regret that not only are rural industries no longer rural, but that the character of a way of life that has been pursued for so many centuries has almost gone. When we speak of rural life we are referring to activities which were related to the rural economy, the descendants of the occupations which supplied the requirements of the medieval rural society. For better or for worse, rural thinking has also changed. The degree of change becomes apparent whenever we see photographs dated, say, 1890–1910. The older way of the land, what Massingham called 'the wisdom of the fields', was determined by the pace of ox and horse. Even after the advent of mechanised farming, it was slow to die, and it is only within the last thirty years that the waggon and the cart have finally gone.

During the nineteenth century a great variety of waggons and carts were produced, the designs coming to be recognised as peculiar to each region. The use of the four-wheeled waggon was confined to lowland farms where the crops of corn, fruit, vegetables and hops were heavy enough to require large vehicles. On the upland farms, the crops of corn and hay were light enough for two-wheeled carts and even sleds to be adequate.

The displacement of the ox by the horse was so gradual that any changes in vehicles and equipment were hardly noticed. But when the open-field cultivation gave place to enclosure and rotation, the waggon came into full use and it is from this time of change that the waggon may be dated. Since then the various types and designs have evolved, creating a complex pattern of distribution over the whole country.

In this distribution of waist- and straight-bed designs, of bow-raves and sheer-raves, of large eastern carts and smaller western ones, of wheels broad and narrow, the king-pin of the pattern appears to have been Banbury, in Oxfordshire. There could hardly have been at any time an awareness of this accident, but the fact does remain that if all the various designs are set out on a map, the location of a king-pin becomes apparent. Certainly Banbury was a meeting place of eight main roads and the history of the town is older than the Banbury Lane that extended from Stamford to Gloucester and beyond. The cock-horse that someone rode to Banbury Cross was the horse which was attached to a waggon team to help it up the long hill on the Warwick road. At the top of the hill the horse was detached and horse and rider would return 'light' to the foot of the hill at the Cross.

Most of the characteristics in design could be traced mainly to orientation in culture. Thinking has always tended to flow along a valley or ridgeway, rather than across at right angles. Some of these orientations will reveal themselves when one studies a small-scale map.

The variety of designs was far too diverse to be explained by the factors of topography and land-use. A not dissimilar situation obtained in the vernacular ways of building farmhouses and cottages, although a direct comparison between house and vehicle will not produce the required clue. Whereas in building local materials were always used, in wheelwrighting the same range of materials, oak, ash, elm and iron, was universal. In building we find a diversity in the use of materials. A stone house on the

Pennines is different from one on the Cotswolds or in Devon. A timber-frame house in Kent is different from one in Shropshire.

So the reason for the variety is to be found in the way of thinking and living, conditioned by the environment in each of the regions. In total, this vernacular is derived from the peculiar individuality of the people of Britain, an individuality that beds ill with 'system' and regimentation in thinking.

The men who made saddles or laid hedges were not always conscious of being craftsmen, however sincerely they worked, but overall they had a pride in the job. Mr Goodchild of Naphill, Buckinghamshire, who in his day made Windsor chairs as well as they have ever been made, told me that he considered himself a skilled workman, rather than a craftsman, but that is the way of a modest man. Whatever methods of mass-production were lately used by the large firms, the village wheelwrights continued to make their products 'one by one'. They had only templates for the curved parts and the rest they did freehand, using a two-foot rule and an inherited knowledge. They certainly had various devices to aid them and most of their tools looked medieval in origin.

Long before the turn of this century there were portents of major importance: the importation of foreign wheat, the winter of 1879–80 and the strange machines that groped an uncertain way across the fields. Henceforth it would not be the horse which set the pace but the internal combustion engine.

1 Types of Waggon and Cart

When did carts and waggons evolve into so many designs? As the medieval open fields became enclosed into small units the wheelwrights, whose forefathers had been serfs, became master craftsmen, making vehicles which slowly began to show regional differences.

The first practical use of the heavy horse in draught, during the sixteenth century, together with the new type of farming which culminated in crop rotation, enabled the waggon to come into full use. During the eighteenth century, wheelwrights were much involved with problems of draught and lock, to which there were a number of solutions. The problem of lock could have been solved by reducing the fore-wheels to turn under the body. But a small wheel ran 'dead' and had a greater draught than a large one, and the axle-bed had to be kept clear because of deep ruts.

One solution, not universally adopted, was to divide the body midway to enable large wheels to increase their lock, but this obstructed the interior of the body and restricted capacity. A compromise, adopted regionally, was to make not a waisted-bed but a crooked one by dividing and overlapping the sides, giving a shallower indent. The Oxford was the classic example, with a good lock, an excellent draught and only a minimal obstruction to the interior (see Fig 5).

The earliest farm waggons mostly had open-sided bodies, without panelling, but composed of a large number of vertical spindles set close enough to contain hay or sheaves of corn, etc. It must have been acknowledged at an early date that the addition of boards would extend the use of a waggon.

Regional variation in design produced some waggons deep in the body and others that were shallower. The deep waggons had a continuous sheer to the profile, like the deck of a sailing ship, but the shallowest waggons had the hind half of the body-side carried in a bow over the hind-wheels.

At this stage, a clear definition of waggon and cart may be made. A waggon ran on four wheels and a cart on two. Both came to be made in a variety of types and a profusion of designs which were regional in distribution. There were three types of waggon: the harvest-waggon, the hermaphrodite and the trolley. The later drays were forerunners of the tractor-hauled vehicles and, like the spring-carts used in market-gardening, are not considered in the present context. The harvest-waggon could be sub-divided into designs as follows:

1 Straight bed with sheer-raves or bow-raves
2 Crooked bed with bow-raves
3 Waisted bed with sheer-raves or bow-raves
4 Boat-waggon with sheer-raves
5 Barge-waggon with sheer-raves

Carts may be divided into tipping and non-tipping. The tip-carts had hinged bodies and the non-tipping had low-loading shallow bodies. The tip-cart in its essential form apparently dated from the fifteenth century. The Scottish wheelwrights, between Clyde and Solway and in the north-east, developed the cart almost to its maximum potential during the nineteenth century, giving it a deep, roomy body with locking devices and large ladders to fore and aft.

When many Scottish farmers brought their carts to East Anglia late in the nineteenth century (see p 118), there followed a widespread acceptance of what came to be known as the 'Scotch cart'. Eventually it was in use everywhere in the eastern half of England down to the south-east coast, but it did not spread very far to the western half. It is probable that in the west the preference for smaller carts and shallower waggons told against the deeper eastern designs. Furthermore, in the west and Wales there was a variety of low-loading types, much used on the hill farms. Tip-carts, of regional design, were as follows:

1	Scotch cart	East coast counties
2	Butt-cart	Devon and Lancashire (Bowland)
3	Moss-cart	South Lancs
4	Box-cart	Wales and Devon
5	Woad-cart	Lincs
6	Trumbel	Wales
7	Dobbin-cart	Hereford

Non-tipping carts, of regional design, were:

1	Wain or Ladder-cart	Cornwall, Devon
2	Long-cart	Wales, north England and Scotland
3	Harvest-cart	Southern and western England
4	Curry- or Kerry-cart	Devon
5	Gambo	Wales
6	Wheelcar	Radnorshire

The hermaphrodite was peculiar to the region between the east coast and Rugby. It was devised as a means of increasing the capacity of a Scotch cart, and consisted of the body and wheels of a cart and the fore-wheels and shafts of a waggon. A vertical structure was added to the fore-carriage, on which rested a specially made long ladder. After harvest the hermaphrodite could be dismantled, leaving the tip-cart ready for winter use.

The trolley, used in the region centred on Herefordshire, could be described as a large, overall harvest frame on four wheels. It came into use much earlier than the Oxford Dictionary suggests (1823), so it may have acquired its name many years after it was designed. The harvest-frame, or thripples, was identical with that used on Hereford waggons.

The boat-waggon was quite different, with a low-sided body and running on wheels small enough to permit a three-quarter lock. The main feature of the design was the arrangement of the sides in two lengthwise planks, the lower piece set outward at an angle of 30° to the vertical and the upper piece at 60° so that the top outside edge lay over the wheels. The width of the body was emphasised by the head- and tail-boards being set athwart the sides. The boat-waggon was distributed over much of England south of Bedford and was made in great numbers by the large firms.

During the latter part of the nineteenth century many makers adopted the plank-sided body for cheapness. Most designs nevertheless incorporated certain features from the panel-sided kinds. The Hereford makers, for example, used the elbow standards and finished the sides with the former grooves and put the same fine chamfering on the undercarriages. Little change was made to wheel diameters and in some counties panelled designs continued.

About the turn of the century the large firms began a form of mass-production, further simplifying their products and reducing the fore-wheels to turn under the body. In the ensuing discussions over merits and demerits, someone dubbed the new design a barge. We may never know what craft were in mind.

We expect to find waggons on lowland farms and low-loading carts on upland farms. This was generally the case but there were surprising exceptions inconsistent with topographical features. While a particular design was usually contained in its distribution by high hills or a wide estuary, we may be surprised to find a number of designs within a region of uniform topography and land-use, and again be surprised to find one design in a region of diverse topography and land usage. According to Waiting, who studied these matters during the years between the wars, design was often determined by the willingness or otherwise of farmers to pay for the job. Another factor was 'individuality of character' which has always been a characteristic of British art and thinking. It showed itself in many activities and it may have played a larger part than topography and land-use in determining design. An important feature in the evolution of design has been the fragmentation of the original idea into many. Thus, in farm transport, there evolved the regional designs with their characteristics.

The older, straight-bed waggons were often known as 'quarter-locks', while those with waisted or crooked beds were called 'half-locks'. Tradition was very strong in the regions and decided whether earlier features be perpetuated or not. Some regions retained the bow-rave, while others abandoned it, building deeper bodies. Some regions gave up the broad wheel quite early while others retained it. Oil axles became common in some regions while others retained the wooden axle-tree.

Derived from the same regional individuality was the variety of names for the parts of waggons and carts. It was part of the vernacular in all the art of wheelwrighting. These part names have been set out in Table 1 (p. 11).

The men who used waggons and carts could hardly have been much concerned whether a waggon had spindle sides, was bow-raved or crooked-bedded. They were more likely to be concerned with the ability to turn awkward corners, to carry a good load and be easily loaded. But when we of today consider all the types and designs, some system of definition becomes necessary.

7

2 The Structure of Waggons and Carts

A waggon consisted of a body and an undercarriage which latter included the wheels and shafts. The undercarriage itself was in two parts, the fore-carriage and the hind, joined by a long tongue-pole, freely at the fore-end but rigidly braced at the hind-end. The fore-carriage swivelled freely on an axis, a stout and long iron pin, fitted into a transverse member called a pillow, which was part of the body. In most waggons the body rested by its own weight without attachment to the hind-carriage. In East Sussex and Kent, however, the body was permanently attached.

The attachment in a tip-cart was quite simple, with the body either hinged to the shafts and bolted to the axle-bed, or hinged to the bed, to which the shafts were bolted.

Undercarriage

The fore-carriage consisted of a heavy axle-bed and a lighter bolster. Between these two members were two or four parallel pieces called hounds, braced by keys at the fore-end and carrying usually one but sometimes two slim transverses called slider-bars, which bore freely against the underside of the tongue-pole with the bearing surfaces of each protected by flat iron bars. The shafts were attached to the fore-ends of the hounds.

The upper face of the bolster bore freely against the lower face of the pillow, both surfaces of which were very slightly convex to allow for the irregularities in the ground. Their centres were protected by greased bearing plates. Right through pillow, bolster, tongue-pole and axle-bed ran the main-pin, usually $1\frac{1}{4}$in in diameter and normally inserted from top to bottom, but sometimes inverted.

In many of the late designs with small fore-wheels, flat iron turn-table rings were fitted for stability in the absence of tongue-pole and slider-bar, and even tongue-poled waggons were sometimes so fitted.

The hind-carriage consisted of an axle-bed and bolster which had a level top surface. Between them were secured the pole and braces, one a side, from a point near the slider-bar back to the outer parts of the bolster and bed. Axle-arms of case-hardened iron were bolted at each end of the axle-beds, except on the early waggons where the beds and arms were of one piece of beech, called an axle-tree. In both types, the arms were set to point downward at an angle which corresponded to the dish of the wheels. The iron arms tapered from $2\frac{3}{4}$in to $1\frac{5}{8}$in diameter and the wooden arms from 5in to 3in, the bearing surfaces of which were sheathed with iron. The iron arms had tails which were secured to the bed by heavy bolts and nuts.

After the introduction of case-hardened iron in 1803, the iron arms were gradually adopted in the face of much head-shaking. Wooden axle-trees were practically indestructible and any wear was met by replacing the iron cleats. With the iron arms, unless regular attention was paid, dried-up grease could cause seizure and the friction caused the iron to crystallise, making the iron so brittle that a sudden jolt would cause fracture. The arm could be retempered before this happened by bringing it to white heat and plunging it in raw flax oil (linseed oil). Some men argued, and still do, that a wheel ran better on a wooden arm, but we must bear in mind that the actual bearing surfaces were iron-to-iron.

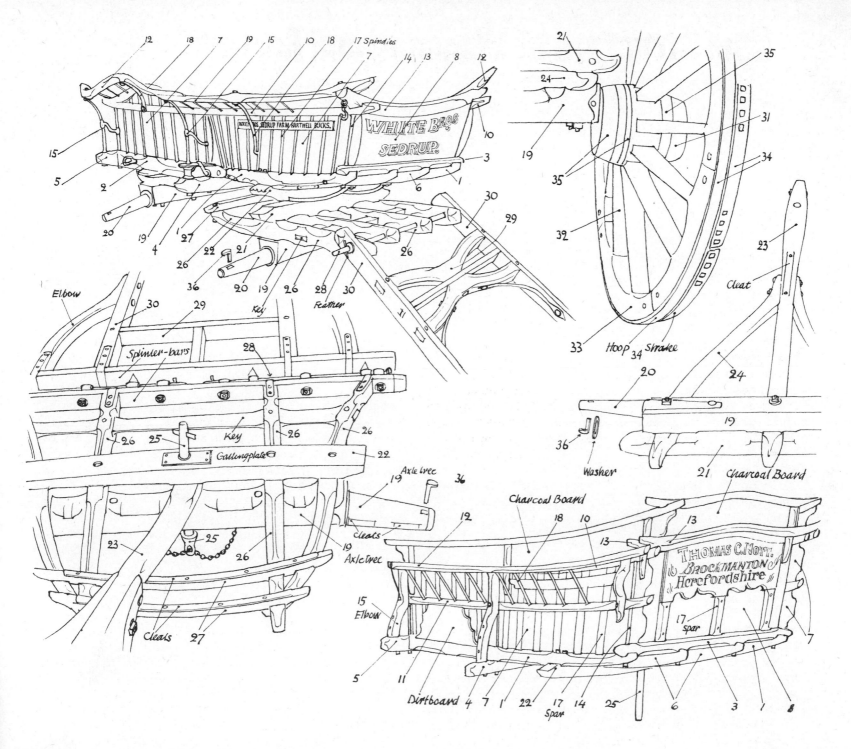

1 Parts of waggons (*see Table 1 for key to diagrams*)

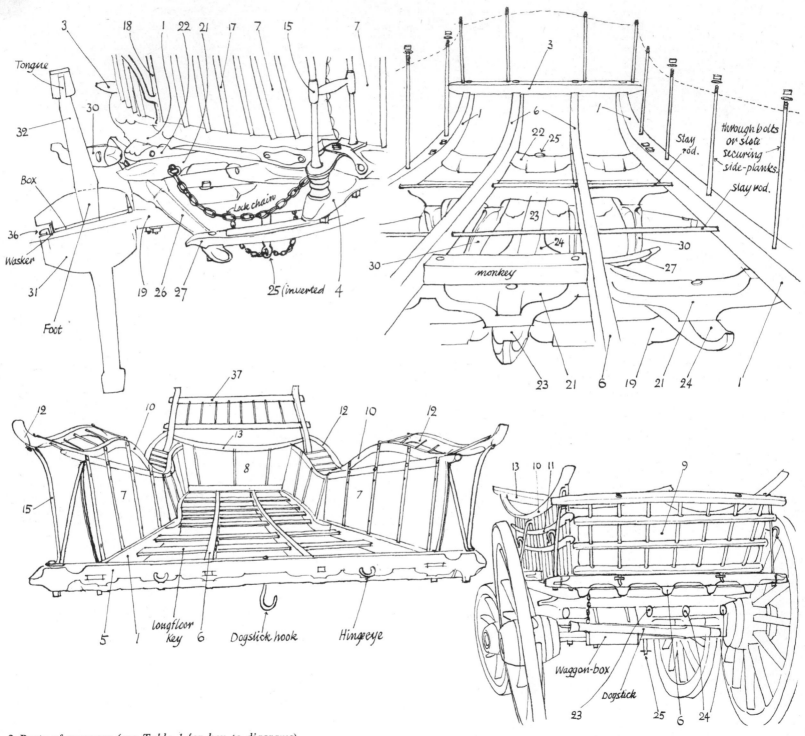

Tongue

32

30

Box

36

Washer

31

Foot

3 18 1 22 21 17 7 15 7

Lock chain

19 26 27

25 (inverted 4

3

1 6 1

Stay rod.

through bolts
or slote
securing
side-planks.

stay rod.

22 25

23

24

30

30

monkey

27

23 21 6 19 21 24 1

37

12 10 12 10 12

13

8

15 7 7

15

5 1 Longfloor
Key 6 Dogstick hook Hingeeye

13 10 11 9

Waggon-box

Dogstick

23 25 6 24

2 **Parts of waggons** (*see Table 1 for key to diagrams*)

	Kent	Sussex	Surrey	Cotswolds	Banbury	Gloucester	Hereford	Hertford	Northampton	Holland	Lindsey
	H. Heathfield Ashford	G. Weller Sompting	G. Sturt Farnham	G. Swainston Stow-on-the-Wold	F. Sumner Cropredy	W. H. J. Drew Frampton Cotterell	N. Wheeler Fownhope	G. W. Casbon Barley	L. W. Phillips Flore	J. P. Bingham Long Sutton	R. C. Dobbs Donnington-on-Bain
1	Sole	Crook	Sidepiece	Crook	Front Crook	Blade	Bedpiece	Side	Main Side	Sole	Sheer
2	Hindsole	Side		Side	Hind Side				Short Side		
3	Cap Piece	Front Dware	Fore Shutlock	Nosepiece	Nosepiece	Under Head	Front Crossledge	Forebridge	Nosepiece	Dress Piece	Front Vardbreed
4	Middle Dware	Middle Dware	Main Beam	Crossledge	Middle Crossbed	Middle Bridge	Middlebed Piece	Crossbar	Middle Crossbridge	Middle Cross Bearer	Middle Vardbreed
5	Hind Dware	Hind Dware	Hind Shutlock	Spreader Piece	Hind Crossbed	Tail Bridge	Back Crossledge	Hind Bridge	Hind Crossbridge	Hindbuck	Hind Vardbreed
6	Middle Sole	Summer	Summer	Runner	Runner	Summer	Summer Rail	Summer	Middle Piece	Middlefill or Sole	Middle Tree
7	Panel Board	Panel Board	Panel Board	Side Board	Side Board	Side Board	Side Board	Side Board	Side Panel	Panel Board	
8	Panel Board	Front Panel Board	Head Board	Front Board	Front Board	Head Name Board	Front Board	Front Board	Front Board	Front Board	Fore-Door
9	Hind Hawk	Tail Bd. or Hawk	Tail Board	Arch	Tail Board	Tail Board	Tail Board	Tail Board	Tail Board	Tail Board	
10	Lade	Top Body Lade	Top Rave	Long Rath	Rave Rail	Rave	Bed Rave	Main Rave	Top Rail	Top Runner	
11	Middle Lade	Middle Lade	Middle Rave			Dripple	Middle Bed Rave	Middle Rave	Body Rail	Middle Runner	Rung
12	Ladeboard	Outside Lade	Out Rave	Wheel Bow	Wheel Bow	Hoop & Horn	Barge Rave	Top Rave	Rave Rail	Outside Runner	
13	Front Hawk	Bridle	Head Piece		Forebuck	Head	Front Bull Rave		Forebuck	Front Top-piece	Fore-Door Cap
14		Clip	Running Pin	Corner Bar	Side Iron	Head Stave	Slote				
15	Shore Stave	Shore Staff/N. Iron	Staff	Standard		Strouts/Spur Iron	Elbow	False Stuck	Crutch	Shore Stake	
16	Crook	Strouter	Strouter		Standard	Strout		Full Standard	Crutch		
17	Stave	Staff	Stretcher		Spar	Flat		Side Standard	Stave	Spindle	
18		Shore Stay	Stay		Rave Iron	Y Stay	Side Stay		Rave Iron	Stay	
19	Axle Bed	Axle Bed	Exbed		Bed	Axle Case	Axle Bed	Bed	Axle Bed	Axle Bed	Axle Bed
20	Arm	Arm	Arm	Arm	Arm	Grease Axle	Axle	Arm	Arm	Axle Arm	Axle Arm
21	Carriage Bolster	Bottom Pillow	Bolster		Bottom Bolster	Carriage Bolster	Guide Bolster	Bottom Pillow	Bolster	Carriage Bolster	Carriage Bolster
22	Top Bolster	Top Pillow	Pillow		Top Bolster	Body Bolster	Bed Bolster	Top Bolster	Body Bolster	Top Bolster	Top Bolster
23	Swimmer Pole	Waggon Pole	Tongue Pole	Tun Pole	Tail Pole	Centre Pole	Carriage Pole	Tongue Pole	Tail Pole	Carriage Pole	Carriage Pole
24		Brace	Spreader	Wing	Spreader	Side Stay	Hip	Tongue	Tail Brace	Side Shear	Side Shear
25		Perch Bolt	Round Pin		Master Pin	Main Pin	Dropper Pin	Perch Bolt	Master Pin	Carriage Bolt	
26	Hound	Hound	Hound		Guide	Carriage Blade	Guide	Guide	Main Guide	Carriage Shear	Carriage Shear
27	Bridge Bar	Slider	Sweep	Slider	Slider	Slide Bar	Slider	Slide Bar	Slide	Brigtree	Brigtree
28	Rod Pin	Draught Bar	Limmer Bolt		Shaft Bar	Shaft Pin	Guidehead*	Shaft Pin	Draught Pin	Shaft Bolt*	
29	Shutter	Rod Key	Bolt	Shuth	Shuttle	Shaft Bar	Cross Piece	Shickle Bar	Shaft Bar	Slat	Slot
30	Rod	Rod	Sharp	Sharve	Sharp	Shaft	Shaft	Shaft	Shaft	Shaft	Shaft
31	Nave	Nave	Stock	Stock	Hub	Nave or Stock	Stock	Nave	Hub	Nave	Nave
32	Spoke	Spoke	Spoke	Spoke	Spoke	Spoke	Spoke	Spoke	Spoke	Spoke	Spoke
33	Felloe	Felloe	Felloe	Felloe	Felloe	Felloe	Felloe	Felloe	Felloe	Felloe	Felloe
34	Tyre	Tyre/Strake	Tyre/Strake	Tyre/Strake	Tyre/Strake	Tyre/Strake	Tyre/Strake	Tyre/Strake	Tyre/Strake	Tyre	Tyre
35	Bond	Nave Bond	Bond	Bond	Bond	Stock Hoop	Bond	Nave Hoop	Bond	Nave Hoop	
36	Linch Pin	Linch Pin	Linch Pin	Linch Pin	Linch Pin	Linch Pin	Linch Pin	Linch Pin	Linch Pin	Axle Pin	
37	Pole	Harvest Pole	Ladder	Gate	Ladder	Ladder	Thripples	Ladder	Ladder	High Raves	Shelvings
							*Splinter-bar			*Splinter-bar	

Table 1 Key to Figs 1 and 2, showing the various parts of waggons

Some decades later came the one-piece 'through axle'. It was actually supplied in two halves to be cut and forged to suit the track of the waggon. It could very easily get bent through impact with obstructions such as tree stumps, unless supported by the wooden bed it was intended to replace.

Once iron arms were accepted the áxle-beds, now of oak, were made a little slimmer, with the tails of the arms sunk flush. Even to a skilled man the setting out of the beds and arms must have been an easier task. Some men, such as Weller of Sompting, in Sussex, worked this out by mathematics, while others worked by eye, rule of thumb and a knowledge passed down. It was part of the craft that these men worked by such methods. All they had was a two-foot rule and an age-old instinct.

Lubrication of wood and iron axles was with animal grease, applied when the wheels were put on, or 'hung'. Neglect would cause seizure and a great deal of trouble. Late in the nineteenth century the oil-axle was devised to improve lubrication by oil instead of grease, but the adoption was not widespread except on road vehicles. An inexpert carter could easily 'cross' the threads or a loose cap could be lost. A waggon so fitted can be detected by the brass cap, which screwed on to the wheel box, covering the modified linch pin.

Wheels

A wheel consisted of a nave or hub, an even number of spokes and a rim composed of segments called felloes, one to every two spokes. The axle-hole was lined with a case-hardened iron 'box' and the wheel was secured to the arm by a washer and linch pin which fitted vertically into a slot at the nose of the arm. The rim of felloes was shod with wrought iron, either in segments equal to the felloes in length and overlapping the joins, or in a continuous hoop. The segments were called strakes in any part of the country.

The nave was made from a solid block of long-seasoned elm. The dimensions of the finished nave varied from a diameter of 12–15in and a depth, from front to back, of 13–15in. Only elm, with its twisty grain, could withstand years of stress. There were ten to fourteen deep holes for the spokes and the wide, tapering hole for the axle through the centre.

Some naves were drum-like in shape, but the majority had a taper from the spoke-face to the back and a greater taper toward the nose. In front of the spokes and on the back there were iron bonds, about 2in or a little less in width, which were shrunk on hot, always *after* the spokes had been fitted. Sometimes there was an extra bond, about ¾in wide, just behind the spokes. A number of very lately made naves were of the van or coach type with a bond on the nose, leaving a slot for the linch-pin. In the same slot

on the waggon type a stopper was fitted for appearance, and secured by a clasp.

The holes for the spokes were cut through to the axle-hole and the corners were cleared with a V-chisel called a buzz. The early spokes had feet tapering from the rectangular section of the spoke but the later ones had tenoned feet which required slimmer holes and therefore a smaller diameter of nave. In most wheels the spokes were set in one line around the nave but many of the later narrow wheels had staggered spoke lines. After the spokes had been knocked in and the angles checked the tongues were made to fit the felloes. They were not in line with the spokes but radial to the centre line of the wheel. In the early wheels these tongues were cut square but in later wheels they were round. Many of the very late mass-produced vehicles had cast iron naves on oil-axles and the name of the wheelwright was cast on the face by the foundry.

Spokes were always made of oak, cleft radially from the block, with the heart at the back. Excepting the very late cheap spokes, they were never sawn out, because cleft wood is stronger, since it naturally cleaves with the grain. The spokes were chamfered between nave and felloe with a half-round on the back and a tapering front. This chamfer eliminated unnecessary wood. There was a perceptible taper in thickness from the nave and a more noticeable taper in depth from about 3½in to about 3in, making the spokes lighter at their ends.

The rim was composed of one felloe for every two spokes. Felloes were usually made of ash, though beech was not unknown. In the meeting ends of the felloes holes were made, about 1in in diameter and about 2in in depth. A dowel, cleft from heart of oak, was inserted in one end of each felloe. As each felloe was knocked onto the spokes each dowel had to engage its opposite hole, thus preserving alignment around the rim. The felloes of broad wheels were strengthened by thin bolts. The felloes were cut from patterns according to the diameter and tread of the wheels. The outer face was the sole and the inner was the belly and the depth varied, being greater for narrow wheels. The belly of a narrow wheel was wider than the sole for greater strength at the spoke holes, but broad felloes were D-shaped (see Fig 3).

The linch pin for an axle of wood was about ¾in square in the shank, while the pin for an iron arm was slimmer, about ⅝in, but about 1in in depth. Both had a flat L-shaped head which rested on the arm. A waggon equipped with a roller-scotch brake had the nearside hind linch-pin extended to an eye to take the chain-hook, so that the roller trailed behind the wheel.

Wheels that ran on iron arms had a single box right through but those running on wood arms had two boxes, bearing on iron cleats

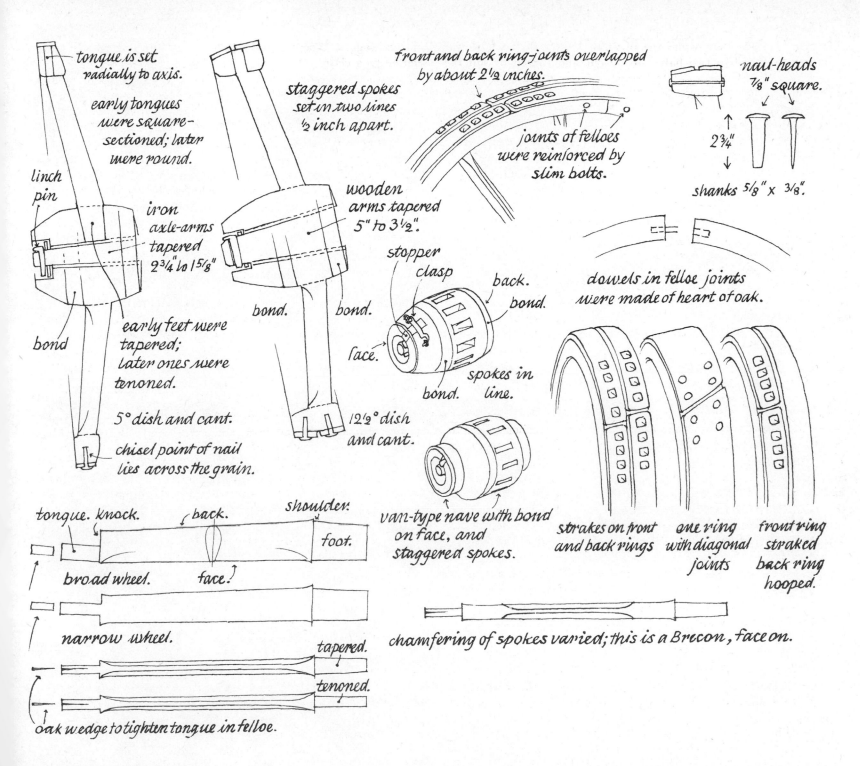

tongue is set radially to axis.

early tongues were square-sectioned; later were round.

linch pin

iron axle-arms tapered 2¾" to 1⅝"

bond

early feet were tapered; later ones were tenoned.

5° dish and cant.

chisel point of nail lies across the grain.

staggered spokes set in two lines ½ inch apart.

wooden arms tapered 5" to 3½".

bond.   bond.

12½° dish and cant.

front and back ring-joints overlapped by about 2½ inches.

joints of felloes were reinforced by slim bolts.

stopper clasp

back. bond.

face.

bond.   spokes in line.

van-type nave with bond on face, and staggered spokes.

nail-heads ⅞" square.

2¾"

shanks ⅝" x ⅜".

dowels in felloe joints were made of heart of oak.

strakes on front and back rings

one ring with diagonal joints

front ring straked back ring hooped.

tongue. knock.   back.   shoulder.

foot.

broad wheel.   face.

narrow wheel.

tapered.

tenoned.

oak wedge to tighten tongue in felloe.

chamfering of spokes varied; this is a Brecon, face on.

3 Structure of wheels

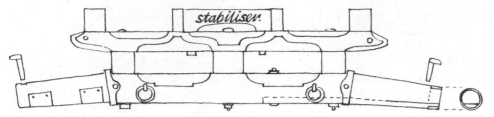

hind axle-tree with cleats on the left arm and bar on the right.

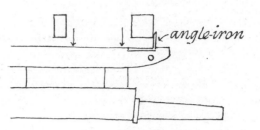

loose bodied waggons were fitted with various types of stabiliser. the angle-iron was most common.

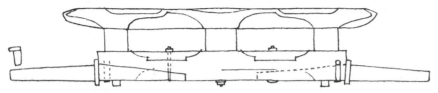

hind axle-bed with iron axle-arms, with tails sunk in the bed.

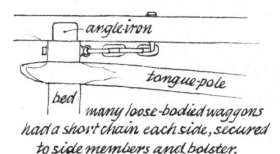

many loose-bodied waggons had a short chain each side, secured to side members and bolster.

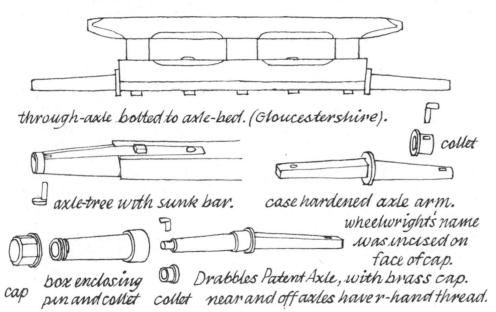

through-axle bolted to axle-bed. (Gloucestershire).

axle-tree with sunk bar.

case hardened axle arm.

wheelwright's name was incised on face of cap.

cap   *box enclosing pin and collet*   *collet*   *Drabbles Patent Axle, with brass cap. near and off axles have r-hand thread.*

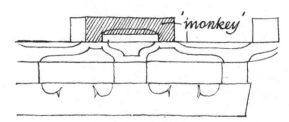

most Hereford and Salop waggons had a 'monkey', or block, fitting between the summers, but a few had a groove in the bolster, corresponding with the sides and summers.

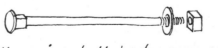

waggons fitted with a roller-scotch usually had an eye extension on near-hind linch-pin for roller chain-hook.

all carriage bolts had square nuts

coach screws, often called 'nut-heads' were turned with a spanner.

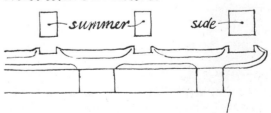

4 Details of types of axle-bed

fitted to the under (bearing) surface of the arm. Some wooden arms had an iron bar on the under-surface with a tail extending under the axle-bed, to which it was bolted. The bearing surface of the countersunk bar conformed to the arm and was secured at the nose by a collar. The bolts which held the bar or the iron arm ran right through the whole assembly of carriage members and had nuts varying from $1\frac{1}{4}$ to 2in square. All carriage bolt nuts were square, not hexagonal. The earliest wheels and all broad wheels were shod with strakes held in position by nails with domed or conical heads. The shank of a nail was about $2\frac{1}{2}$in long by a section $\frac{1}{2}$in by $\frac{1}{4}$in, tapering to a chisel point $\frac{3}{16}$in wide. The heads were $\frac{3}{4}$in square. The nail holes in the strakes were punched while hot and were usually in groups of four with a distance over each group of about $6\frac{1}{2}$in. Many wheels had odd numbers of nails, quite unaccountably, because the nail-holes were made beforehand. The nails were always put in with the chisel *across* the grain to avoid splitting the felloe. Broad wheels with two rings of strakes had each ring staggered to give an overlap at the joins of about 2in. This gave a continuous iron surface to the wheel. A very few broad wheels were shod with a single ring of strakes on the tread of the wheel. They had diagonal joins and were secured with groups of four flush-headed nails at each end.

It was usual to put coned strakes on the outside or front ring and flat ones on the inside or back ring, giving the tread a slightly domed section, making the running easier. In Gloucestershire and adjacently, the back ring was usually hoop shod, it being claimed that this caused less damage to grassland. A further advantage was that the hoop, bearing directly on the spokes, bound the wheel better. A glance at the diagram of felloe section will show that the spokes in a broad wheel entered the felloes nearer to the back than the front (see Fig 3).

Narrow wheels up to 4in were later shod with hoops, shrunk on hot and secured at three points with small nails. The bars for both strakes and hoops were about 18ft long and $\frac{5}{8}$ or $\frac{3}{4}$in thick. A wheel called a traveller was run around the sole of the wheel and then retraced on the bar with an allowance for contraction in proportion to the diameter. The straight bar was then cut with a cold sett (chisel) and sledge and put through the tyre bender, which resembled a very robust mangle. It required the greatest skill to avoid any twist and to ensure that the ends met truly. The scarfed ends were forged together at welding heat. Once again, the craftsman's experience ensured a hoop that would contract dead tight.

The bars were supplied in various widths to suit the treads. With a 6in wheel it was usual to have two rings each $2\frac{3}{4}$in wide, but I have found variations with 3in and $2\frac{3}{4}$in or 3in and 3in. One $6\frac{1}{2}$in wheel I measured had $3\frac{3}{4}$in and $2\frac{3}{4}$in treads. Wheels up to 3in or $3\frac{1}{2}$in were not coned, but flat. Over that size they were coned as described.

The trend during the nineteenth century was toward narrower treads. As late as 1850 some waggons were built with 9in wheels with three rings of strakes, yet it was about this time that the Oxford, running on $2\frac{1}{2}$in wheels, came to be recognised as the lightest running of all waggons. The changeover, like that from ox to horse, was an uneven and irregular process. While no broad wheels were made in Devon after 1850, they continued to be made in Herefordshire until 1930. It was not merely a matter of progress. A broad wheel may have been hard on the horses but it was more sure-footed on wet, heavy soil on hillsides.

The gait of a walking draught horse in the shafts set up a lateral weaving motion that was transmitted to the wheels, causing them to run 'off and back' on the arms, first the near then the off, sounding the once-familiar 'click-clack' knocking. On the uneven surfaces of fields and lanes there was also the irregular thrusting from the rough ground. All this was partially offset by the axle-arms being set about $\frac{3}{16}$in forward, making the wheels slightly pigeon-toed.

If we look at any waggon end-on we shall notice that the wheels lean outward instead of standing vertically. The degree of lean or cant varies but the axle line corresponds, and then we notice that the spokes of the wheels are not flat but dished or angled on the axle line. In any one set of wheels all these angles are the same, resulting in the bottom or lowest spokes being nearly vertical—in order to resist the on and off thrust. The angles of dish and cant varied from $2\frac{1}{2}°$ in a flattish narrow wheel to 5° and then right up to as much as $12\frac{1}{2}°$ in a deeply dished broad wheel. A waggon with well made, well hung wheels, whatever the tread or dish, would have considerable momentum once set in motion, and the large diameters were a major factor.

A not unimportant factor concerning deeply dished wheels was that the greater outward lean from a reasonable wheel track gave a greater clearance between the sides of a straight-bed waggon and its wheels, thus allowing a better lock. A point I have not seen in print is that a deeply-dished wheel will have its ground contact closer to a vertical from the edge of the axle-bed, putting less strain on the arm.

Before the term 'track' was accepted to mean the distance between opposite wheels, wheelwrights would speak of wheels being *x* inches at ground. Some confusion arose because certain scholars took the measurement *between* the treads, while others meant *over*. It is usual now to say '*x* inches over' to avoid any possible confusion.

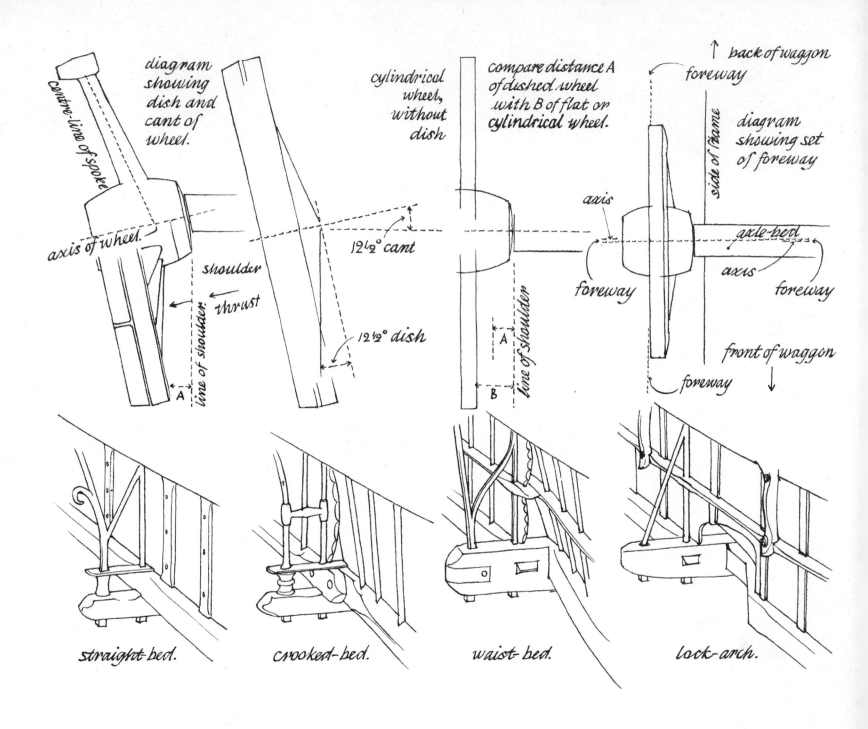

5 Dish, cant and foreway in wheels, and types of bed

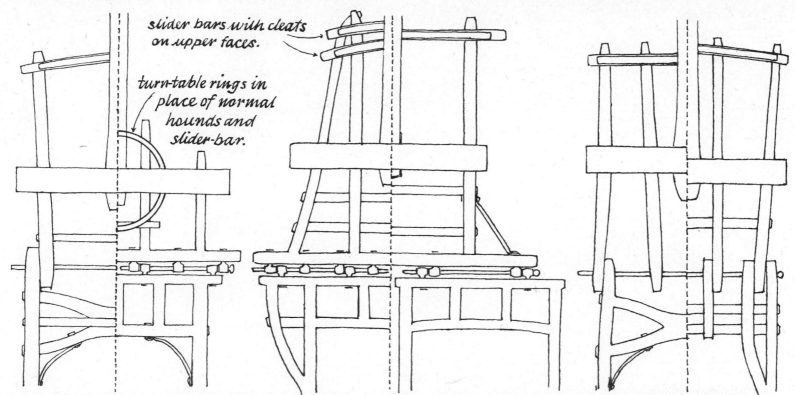

slider bars with cleats on upper faces.

turn-table rings in place of normal hounds and slider-bar.

Six examples of the many arrangements of fore-carriage members with either draught-pin alone or with splinter bars and draught-pins.

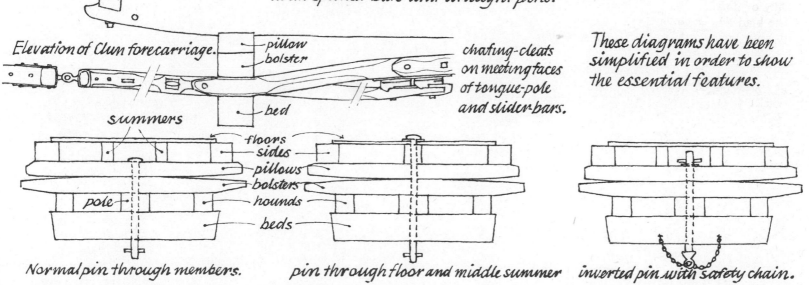

Elevation of Clun forecarriage.

pillow
bolster
bed

summers

chafing-cleats on meeting faces of tongue-pole and slider-bars.

These diagrams have been simplified in order to show the essential features.

floors
sides
pillows
bolsters
hounds
beds

pole

Normal pin through members.

pin through floor and middle summer

inverted pin with safety chain.

6 Fore-carriages. (These diagrams have been simplified in order to show the essential features)

Shafts

The shafts were attached to the fore-carriage by either of two systems. In one, the butt-ends overlapped the fore-ends of the hounds and were held by a $\frac{3}{4}$in round rod. In the second, the shaft butts and the hound fore-ends each were capped by transverses called splinter-bars, each of which had a corresponding set of barrel hinges. Some splinter-bars were as much as 72in across and two sets of shafts could be attached.

Where the shafts were hinged by draught-pin the hounds were approximately parallel but when a 72in bar was fitted then there were four hounds, the inner more or less parallel but the outer splayed forward to just clear the wheels before meeting the bar. Behind the axle-bed the outer hounds closed in to meet the inner.

A single draught-pin was usually inserted from the offside, though some photographs contradict this. Where double shafts were fitted then the pins were inserted from each side. A pair of shaft blades was cut from the same length of ash, which was resistant to the stresses received by members unsupported at their extremities. The blades were joined at their butt ends by a set of keys, variously arranged and braced by ironwork. In the Marches, where the splinter-bar was almost universal, the single shafts were strengthened by external elbows. In single draught-pinned shafts we may note that several wheelwrights, such as Gerring of Milton, near Didcot, and Blank of Bradwell, Essex, set their shafts *between* the hounds. Near the toes of the blades of all shafts there were sets of hooks and staples to take the harness. The ridge-chain, usually of double twist links, was attached on the off staple.

The blades tapered from 3–4in square at the butt to 3in by 2in at the toe, giving strength at the butt and lightness at the toe.

Remembering that early waggons and carts designed for ox draught had a central draught pole, it is of interest that many Yorkshire waggons had this feature until the end of the nineteenth century for horse draught.

The hounds had a varying section through their length, about $3\frac{1}{2}$in square from the shafts to the bed, behind which they tapered to their tail ends where they supported the slider-bar. This was usually, but not always, curved to give a constant bearing on the underside of the tongue-pole. The two meeting surfaces were reinforced with chafing cleats, kept well greased. Some fore-carriages had twin slider-bars, reducing friction.

The main-pin, on which the carriage turned, was usually $1\frac{1}{4}$in in diameter. The majority were inserted from the top, through the pillow, bolster, and pole to emerge below the axle-bed, where they were secured with a wedge or feather which fitted tightly in a slot. Where there was a middle summer then the pin went through a plate on the floorboard. Very often the pin was inverted and inserted from below the bed, and the wedge inserted above the pillow. These pins mostly had large conical heads, either with rings (the Marches) or hooks (Kent) through which a slender safety chain was passed and then stapled to the bed.

Wheelwrights were accustomed to using diverse terms in referring to waggons and carts. Just as farming people knew farms as much by the number of horses used, so wheelwrights knew waggons by the width of tread. It is the scholars who term them 'box' or 'bow' waggons.

Where nearly every waggon had wheels with say 3½–4in of tread, the terms 'narrow' and 'broad' being relative would hardly be understood in that region. Sometimes they knew them by their capacity, 2½ tons or 4 tons. In another region, where narrow and broad wheels were each more or less equal, then the term 'broad wheel' or even 'broad waggon' and 'narrow waggon' would be commonly used. Sometimes they spoke of a 6in or a 2½in waggon.

Some terms in common usage in one region would hardly be understood, if at all, in another. The Scotch cart was generally understood in the eastern half of England, but I have heard it referring to a low-loading harvest-cart near Henley-on-Thames. In parts of Wales, too, there was confusion between gambo and long-cart, where either name could mean the other cart. Reference has been made to the track of wheels, their treads, diameters and the conditions of surface on which the vehicles were used. With so many ruts in a state of virtual permanency, whether soft from prolonged rain or crust-hard from summer sun, farm vehicles had to be constructed to run in those ruts, much in the manner of wagons on a railway. Sturt, writing in retrospect on the last years of the nineteenth century, understood this as 'taking the routs'.

Once the vehicles in any one region (or parish) had by custom been built to a given track, that dimension had to be kept to, within an inch or two. Some indication of the variation from region to region may be afforded by comparison of examples.

The Oxfords had a track varying from 62in to 66in over the vast region in which these waggons were used. In Somerset the track varied from 65in to 70in. The remarkably wide Surrey and Hampshire waggons varied from 74in to 77in and in neighbouring Dorset they were generally of 71in. Sussex, however, was nearer the average at 65in. Yorkshire waggons varied from 60in on the Wolds down to no more than 50in in the Dales. The Herefords, with broad wheels set to $12\frac{1}{2}°$ dish on a track of 63–66in looked more mobile and less four-square than the largest of the Suffolk waggons on a slightly wider track. A waggon built to a 63in track could not be used on a track of 77in for danger of oversetting, nor could a vehicle with 36in wheels be used in ruts made by 50in wheels.

In the wettest of soils it did not follow that the depth of the ruts was determined by wheel diameter. If bed-rock was close to the surface the wheels could go no deeper than the rock. Only on deep soils could the wheels sink till the waggon 'scraped its belly' with the axle-bed acting as a sort of bulldozer. The consequence of all this was that wheelwrights were reluctant to reduce the sizes of fore-wheels in order to improve the lock. A comparison may be made between the diameters of fore- and hind-wheels in inches:

	FORE-WHEEL	HIND-WHEEL	TREAD
Oxford	48 –52	60 –62	2½–3
Somerset bow	42 –45	50 –58	3 –6
Dorset late	43 –49	45 –55	3
Hereford	42½–48	52½–59	3 –6½

With all our country lanes now converted into high-speed 'run-ways', one set of problems has given way to another. The problem that confronted wheelwrights lay in building a waggon that had a good draught, could be turned in a reasonable circle, had a floor at a convenient height from the ground and could carry a good load. The tip-cart had to be adaptable and simple to operate. Having made such a waggon or cart, the wheelwright was surely entitled to finish the job with whatever decoration took his fancy. Pride in the job counted for a great deal. Some men exercised restraint while others fairly let themselves go. Since colour has played such an important part in the finish of vehicles, it will not be out of place to remark that the paint, lead oxide based on linseed oil, was an eighteenth-century invention, used primarily to protect the exterior surfaces of the soft wood at that time being increasingly used on houses.

Field gates and fencing of oak do not require such protection, so one may wonder at what period lead oxide paint was first applied to waggons and carts? Were the vehicles originally left bare, or was there some kind of finish, more suitable than pitch. It may be noted that Mr Tedstone of Aymestrey, Herefordshire, has an old waggon that has never received a coat of paint. It stands in a well ventilated shed and the wood is perfectly sound after 70 years.

Much more information on the origins of 'county' colours is required. The writers of the eighteenth and nineteenth centuries wrote copiously on every aspect of agriculture except the vehicles. At best, they made little more than passing reference.

We hear of this or that waggon being blue and the tint most commonly mentioned is Prussian, but in fact there were also Brunswick, Saxe, indigo and a bluish-green. Likewise, we learn that the wheels were red. But which red? Scarlet, orange, Venetian

(red-oxide), salmon or crimson? It is so unusual to find a newly-painted vehicle that one has but poor facilities for decision. Nearly every 'yellow' vehicle I have seen had faded to shades varying from a lime-yellow to an off-white tinged with yellow and the reds varied from near-scarlet to the palest pink. Sometimes a rub with a wet finger could reveal a clue.

Lead oxide (white lead) was always bought from the colour merchants in powder form, in 5cwt barrels, and finally ground by hand with muller and stone and mixed with raw linseed oil to the consistency of thick double cream. A little turpentine was added if any thinning was considered necessary. Likewise, the putty was knocked up with whiting and oil. Paint mixed up but not used was kept under water in a keg. After the priming, any necessary stopping was done with putty, and then followed the successive undercoats and top coats and finally the varnish, but we should note that each paint-shop had its own recipe and method. The branding of name and farm, etc., on the headboard was usually done by a signwriter.

Body

The foundation of the body of a waggon or cart, usually called the bed, consisted of two side-pieces of oak, joined at each end by two cross-pieces of oak, in a cart, with an additional cross-piece midway in a waggon. Parallel to the sides and equidistant between them were lighter-sectioned pieces called summers, which varied in number from one to four, according to design.

In all designs the hind cross-piece was joined by mortice and tenon, and in the majority the fore and the middle, or main, cross-pieces were lap-joined, the fore above and the main below. In the waggons of East Sussex and Kent, however, all parts were joined by mortice and tenon on the same plane and the majority of East Anglian waggons had massive main cross-pieces morticed on the same plane.

Straight-bed waggons had continuous sides, but the crooked-bed and waist-bed waggons had divided sides. In the crooked-bed waggons the fore- and hind-sides were lapped, the fore behind, while the waist-bed waggons had the fore-side turned in more deeply. All joints were secured with carriage bolts of suitable dimensions, but in many waggons the summers were secured by dowels. Certain designs which had lap-joined main crosses had a flat iron bar of the same length above the floor to give a better hold for the iron standards, and certain designs had tie-rods joining opposite sides. In most designs the main and hind crosses projected about 9in each side to give a strong support to the body sides.

Many of the earliest farm waggons and carts were made with open sides, that is without panel boards behind the spindles. The hind end was closed by a removable or hinged tail-board while in most waggons the front was permanently closed with a head-board. Both were open, like the sides. A projecting side-rail was soon added at or slightly above the level of the top rail. There were usually additional rails all round, between the floor-side and the top. The space between the floor and the top was filled by a large number of vertical spindles set closely enough to contain the load. There is a model, made by H. R. Waiting, in the Science Museum, London, which shows how these waggons appeared.

The practice of fitting panel-boards appears to have begun during the eighteenth century. Edward Lisle, of Crux Easton, between Newbury and Whitchurch, commented on this in 1757 in *Observations on Husbandry*. The boards of elm, or of poplar in Sussex, were originally secured to the spindles with greased leather thongs but later they were wired. On waggons where flat spars were fitted, the boards were secured by rose nails, clenched on the inside. The open-sided waggon declined after 1800, though many waggons in East Anglia had panels along the lower half only, a practice continued for long afterwards.

The standards supporting the sides above the main and hind cross-pieces were of wood in some regions or of iron in others, which practices became 'traditional' in their respective regions, with no evidence of any transition from wood to iron. In other regions both were used, sometimes on the same waggon.

Wooden standards were tenoned at their feet into the cross-pieces and secured either by a horizontal bolt or by vertical strap bolts. Iron standards had their feet through the bar and cross-piece with a washer between and held by nuts below. Both types acted as buttresses to the sides and also supported the outer rail which was supported at the fore-end by the head-rail. A few waggons made in the West of England had the main cross-piece ending flush with the sides, with wooden supports held by iron sockets. The designs of both wood and iron supports varied according to the wheelwrights' ideas, making it possible to identify their origin.

Many of the earlier panelled waggons had middle-raves and some had additional supports intermediately above each axle-bed. The later plank-bodied waggons were without spindles or spars or mid-rails. The sides consisted of two planks, edge to edge, of up to 1¾in thickness, secured by vertical 'through rods' holding the whole structure of rails and side pieces together. It should be appreciated that the order of assembly in panelled and plank sides differed. Panel boards were fitted *after* the framework had been constructed, while planks were fitted *during* the construction: The 'through rods' ran down through holes drilled vertically in the section of the planks and were secured with nuts at top and bottom. The number of rods varied from five to eight each side.

The various shapes of principal and intermediate supports gave rise to terms which were descriptive of those shapes. The ash supports of the Hereford waggons were called 'elbows' while those of Shropshire were 'wishbones'. In Sussex the iron intermediates were called 'cupid's bows'. The most common of iron principal standards were the N kind and in Wiltshire there was no mistaking the Y-standard.

While the vast majority of waggons had fixed head-boards, in East Anglia, Essex and Cambridgeshire most of the waggons had two-part head-boards with both parts removable and pegged in position, like tail-boards. Head-boards could be panelled in the same way as the sides or in one piece, without spindles and spars. The top-rail was usually quite robust in section and it was almost invariably the practice to secure it at each side by flat bars to the cross-piece and side-pieces. There were threads at top and bottom for nuts to tighten the structure. The tail-board was hinged to the hind cross-piece either by barrel hinges, so that it could be lowered, or on 'pin and eye' hinges so that it could be removed altogether. This latter was necessary where the ladder rested at floor-level.

The waggons of East Sussex and Kent were unusual in having no tail-board, but a stout wooden bar, called a hawk, was placed across at the level of the top-rails where it was pegged in position, leaving the space below quite open. Either type of hinge had the top extensions long enough to brace the boards and some were turned in an outward curve to terminate in forged rings to fit over the ends of the top-rails, where they were pegged. Others were simply secured by small chains. There was a less common type of light hinge consisting of two eye bolts threaded together. The tail-boards themselves varied a great deal. The most common were the plank type with or without spars bracing, but there were many waggons with top- and bottom-rails, sometimes oval in section with spindles in conformity with those on the side. Such boards were braced with thin rods which were continuations of the eye bolts. These 'tails' were either with or without panels. A curious variant of this was to be found on some of the Montgomery waggons.

In the great majority of waggons there was a continuous sheer to the top of the body, like the deck of a boat, more pronounced in some designs than in others. Such waggons had bodies which were deep enough for the rails to be clear of the hind-wheels. But many bodies were so shallow that the hind part was carried in an arc over the hind-wheel. In some, such as the Oxford, this arc began and finished at the level of the top-rail, to terminate in an upward curl, but in Wiltshire and the Vale of the White Horse the arc was carried down to join the hind cross-piece. In a third design, peculiar to Dorset, Somerset and Devon, the bow did not complete the arc but from a point above the centre line of the

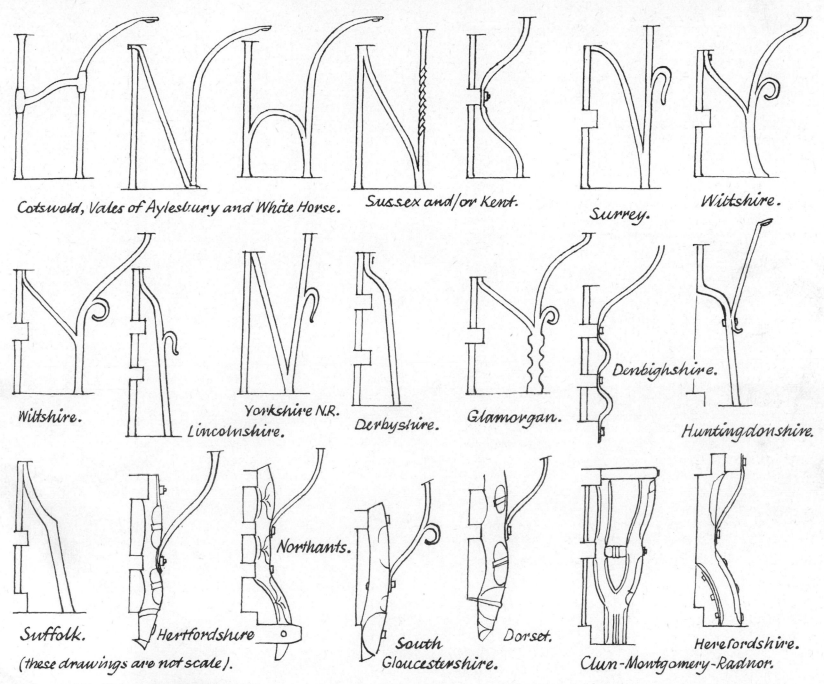

Cotswold, Vales of Aylesbury and White Horse.

Sussex and/or Kent.

Surrey.

Wiltshire.

Wiltshire.

Lincolnshire.

Yorkshire N.R.

Derbyshire.

Glamorgan.

Denbighshire.

Huntingdonshire.

Suffolk.

(these drawings are not scale).

Hertfordshire

Northants.

South Gloucestershire.

Dorset.

Clun-Montgomery-Radnor.

Herefordshire.

7 Some designs of main (or middle) standards

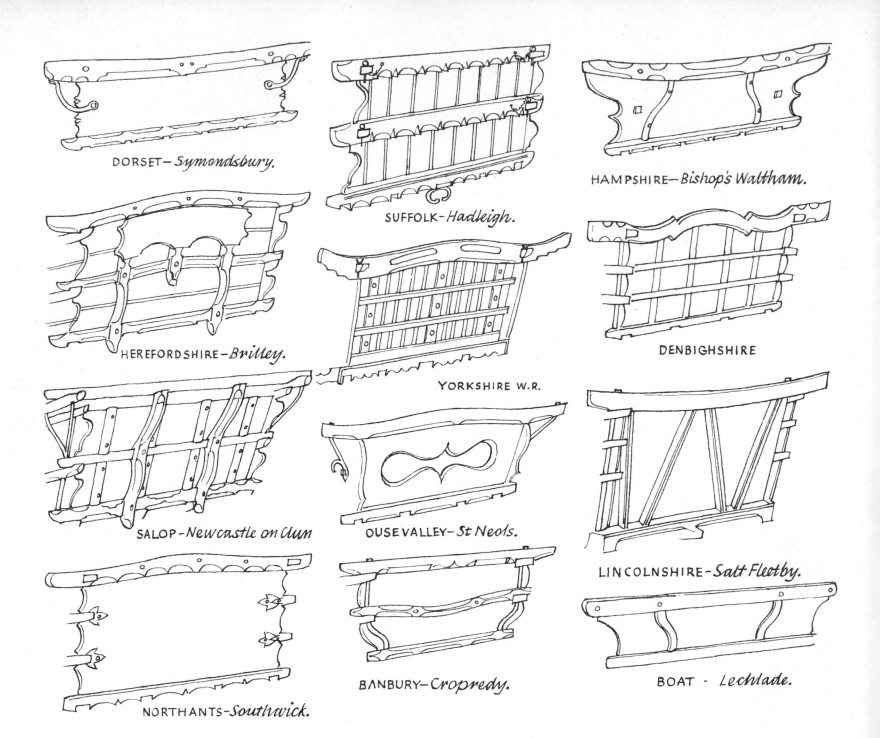

DORSET – *Symondsbury.*

SUFFOLK – *Hadleigh.*

HAMPSHIRE – *Bishop's Waltham.*

HEREFORDSHIRE – *Britley.*

YORKSHIRE W.R.

DENBIGHSHIRE

SALOP – *Newcastle on Clun.*

OUSE VALLEY – *St Neots.*

LINCOLNSHIRE – *Salt Fleetby.*

NORTHANTS – *Southwick.*

BANBURY – *Cropredy.*

BOAT – *Lechlade.*

8 Twelve of the regional designs of head-board

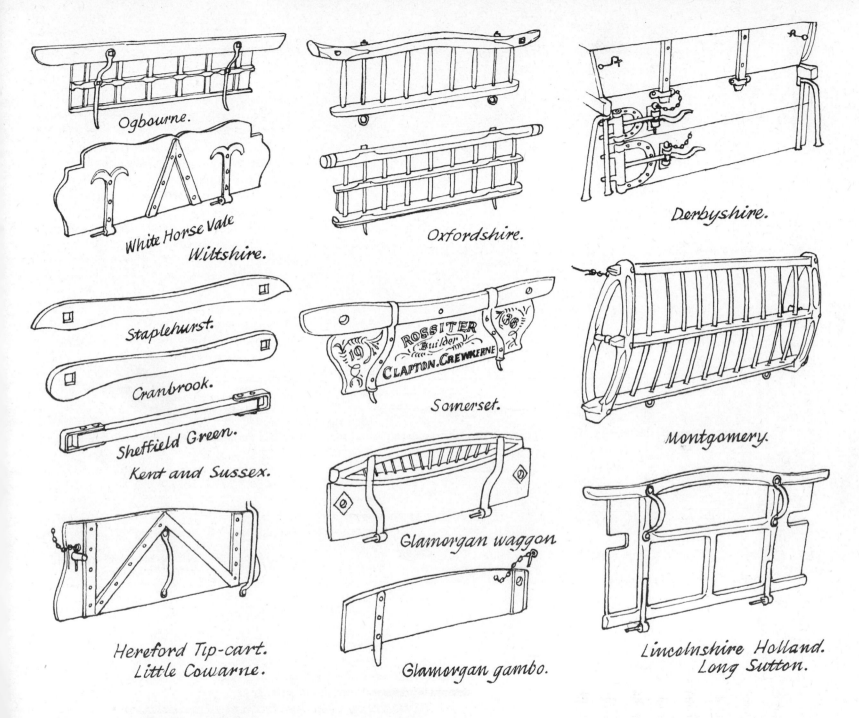

Ogbourne.

White Horse Vale
Wiltshire.

Oxfordshire.

Derbyshire.

Staplehurst.

Cranbrook.

Sheffield Green.

Kent and Sussex.

ROSSITER
Builder
CLAPTON. CREWKERNE

Somerset.

Montgomery.

Hereford Tip-cart.
Little Cowarne.

Glamorgan waggon

Glamorgan gambo.

Lincolnshire Holland.
Long Sutton.

9 Fourteen of the regional designs of tail-board, which varied in design and fitment as much as the remaining parts

23

hind-wheel curved up slightly. This was generally known as a cock-rave. The term 'ship-waggon' (distinct from boat or barge) was sometimes heard, but only in East Devon. In all designs the outer rail followed the curves of the top-rail. The distance between the two varied and also the angle. Those waggons which carried harvest-frames and removable boards had the top and outer rails 1½in apart and to hold the board pegs firmly but the usual distance was about 8in. Neither the Brecon nor the Lincolnshire waggons had out-rails, making them appear narrower than they actually were. The out-rails were supported by the standards and the head-rail and sometimes additionally by thin iron stays which varied in number. Some of the Herefords were unusual in having a row of about ten spindles supporting the rails from the mid-rail. In a great many designs the space between top- and out-rails was filled with thin rods corresponding to the spindles with an opening at the fore-end for the ladder. In many other designs this space was closed by panels called lime boards. The very late designs of barge- and boat-waggon had one-piece planks with no rails. A small number of the old types had an additional rail between top- and out-rail.

Table 2 General distribution of waggons according to the shape of bed, profile of body and width of wheel-tread

	Straight bed		Crooked bed		Waisted bed		Lock arch		
	Broad	Narrow	Broad	Narrow	Broad	Narrow	Broad	Narrow	
Sheer-rave	x						x		E Midlands
						x	x		E Anglia
					x	x			Weald
	x	x	x	x	x	x			Severn
	x	x							Marches
				x	x				Staffs. Derby
	x	x							Wales
							x		Lincoln
	x	x							Yorks
Half-bow			x		x		x		Vale of Aylesbury
			x		x		x		Cotswold
Full-bow						x	x		Berkshire
	x	x	x	x					Severn
	x	x							Wessex
			x						Glamorgan
Cock-rave	x	x							W of England

NOTE: The inevitable exceptions to the rule, to be found in every region, have not been included in this table

Until the last quarter of the nineteenth century the floorboards were made of elm about 1in thick, laid between the sides and summers on a series of transverse keys which were tenoned through the members from side to side. During the last quarter, however, timber merchants were increasing the supply of deal planks of various thicknesses and widths. Henceforth, for the sake of cheapness, these planks 1in thick by 6in wide replaced the long boards. Notwithstanding the uniformity of thickness, it was inevitable that a board would 'ride up' making the use of a shovel, in unloading gravel or coal, etc., a matter of vexation. The planks were laid crosswise on top of the summers and between ledges in the sides. The top edge of long boards was flush with them.

The body was constructed as a unit, separate from the undercarriage, whether it would later be attached or not. We have noted that the fore-pillow was part of the body (and therefore the same colour) and not of the undercarriage, and since the main-pin usually went first through the pillow before entering the fore-carriage, we may presume that the floor was put in after the whole assembly had been completed. This may well have been a reason for some wheelwrights preferring the inverted pin, which could be inserted at the last stage of assembly.

The majority of bodies were 'loose' on the hind-carriage, resting there by their weight and kept in position laterally by stabilisers which varied from region to region. Most Herefords, and some of the Gloucesters, had a stout block of wood, called a monkey, bolted to the top of the hind bolster to fit exactly between the two summers, but in Gloucestershire, certainly south of the city, two iron angle-plates were attached to the top of the bolster to fit exactly outside the side pieces. An alternative in some cases was to cut notches in the bolster about 1½in deep to accommodate the sides and summers. Quite a lot of these loose-bodied waggons had a short length of chain each side attached to the bolster and the underside of the side piece. When the nut was turned home the chain was taut.

Waggons built in the Weald (East Sussex and Kent) had their bodies permanently attached to the hind-carriage and tongue-pole, usually dispensing with pole braces and the bolster. One could tell at first glance by the snug way the body sat between the wheels with just two blocks of wood between the side pieces and axle-bed. The manner in which tip-cart bodies were attached should be noted here. Whereas the sides and shafts of non-tipping harvest-carts were nearly always of one piece, those of tip-carts were obviously in two. There were two types, one commonly found in the eastern half of the country down to Sussex and the other in the western half down to Devon and Wales. In the eastern type the shafts were hinged to the body in front of the axle and the body was bolted directly to the axle-bed and the locking device was in the form of an eccentric bar which held itself in position and had to be lifted to allow the body to tip. In the western type the shafts were bolted to the axle-bed on top of which the body was hinged. The locking device was in the form of a slotted iron bar and peg which held the body. The slots afforded five or six positions of tip angle.

Ironwork

Close examination of any waggon or cart will show whether the iron bar work was of square section or round. Square-sectioned iron was mainly ¾in while round was mostly, but by no means always, of 1in diameter. To some extent, according to regional practice, one can judge the age of the vehicle, but it is as risky as any other guessing about waggons. Originally all iron was square in section giving place to round, with the same irregularity as occurred with changes in wheel treads and from ox and horse. Some regions went over to round quite early, others fairly late, while some continued to use square iron until the very late nineteenth century.

Carriage bolts have long parallel shanks and convex heads and a square collar next to the head to prevent the bolt turning when the nut is tightened. The bolts used by wheelwrights had square nuts a little wider across than the hexagonal engineers' nuts. Wherever a nut came next to a piece of wood a washer was placed in between.

With regard to the fitting of the main-pin, I quote from a letter from J. P. Bingham, a retired wheelwright:

When fitting the centre-pin through the top carriage bolster (pillow) and axle-bed, the holes were bored with a 1¾ or 2 inch bit with a wooden shaft for turning, and the centre bolt was put through red hot so that there would be a certain amount of play for the pin . . . the centre plates (of pillow and bolster) were not flush with the faces of the bolsters but were an eighth of an inch projecting.

That many bolts, especially the early ones, had tapering shanks may be gathered from a letter by Andrew Jewell, keeper of the Museum of English Rural Life, in correspondence with an old wheelwright near Hungerford:

There would be four bolts for the carriage and the two that went down through the pillar, hounds and axle would be about 14 inches long and 1¼ inches at the top (next the head) and 1 inch at the bottom. They would not cut a thread and fit a nut if they could help it, but would punch a key-hole about ⅞ by 3⁄16

inches and fit a washer and key. Then they would bore a hole about 1 inch through the wood, hot the bolt and drive it into the hole to about 1 inch from the top and let it cool. When it was cold they would drive it in with a sledge and drive the key in at the same time. I have seen lots of these taper-bolts and have never seen one work loose. Most wheelwrights used to burn their bolts into place, and if you use wood to hot the iron it is better, for the iron does not burn the wood so much as a coal fire.

All this meant that the acid in oak would corrode the iron unless burned by the hot iron.

Before Whitworth introduced the standard thread, the village smiths tapped their own with nuts to fit and one presumes from the foregoing quotations that many of them preferred to use 'key and slot'.

Reverting to square iron, it may be stated that nearly every smith liked to exercise his skill and artistry by giving any length of bar between joins a spiral twist, made while the iron was cherry-red (discernible in the gloom of the forge).

Brakes

There were three occasions when brakes were required. Firstly, during ascent to prevent a waggon running back. Secondly, during descent to prevent a waggon over-running the horses, and thirdly when a waggon was standing. In work on the road all three types of brake would be used in the course of any journey, but on farm-land they were not used other than when standing.

There were two kinds of brake for ascent. The most commonly fitted was the roller, or scotch. This was of elm, wider than the wheel and about 5in in diameter, bound with iron bonds and rotating on a spindle to which lengths of light chain were fitted. One chain was attached permanently to the axle-bed, while the second chain hung from a hook under the body. At the foot of the hill the waggon was halted and the loose chain was hooked to the eye on the near-side linch pin, so that the roller trailed immediately behind the wheel. A much less common kind was the dog-stick, made of ash, about 36in long and with a middle thickness of about 2in tapering a little toward the ends. One end was permanently attached to the tongue-pole or the hind axle-bed with the loose end held in a large hook. When used, it was let down to trail along the road. The trailing end had a strong iron prong which held against the road surface on halting.

For all narrow-wheeled waggons and a small number of broad wheelers, the descending brake was a large, cast-iron shoe, a little wider than the wheel tread, which was on a long stout chain attached next to the main cross-piece. When not in use the shoe

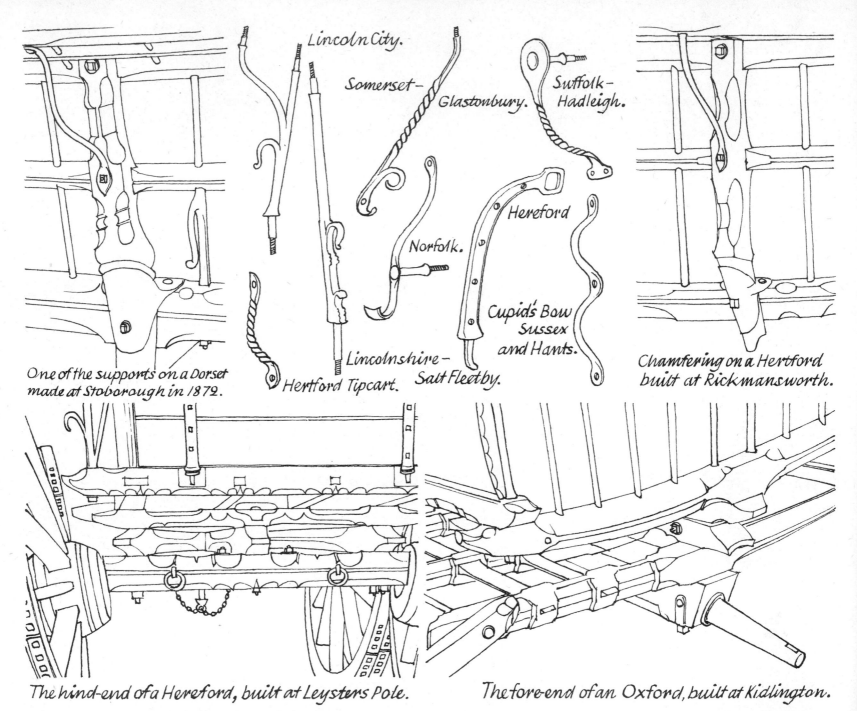

Lincoln City.

Somerset—
Glastonbury.

Suffolk—
Hadleigh.

Norfolk.

Hereford

Cupid's Bow
Sussex
and Hants.

One of the supports on a Dorset
made at Stoborough in 1872.

Hertford Tipcart.

Lincolnshire—
Salt Fleetby.

Chamfering on a Hertford
built at Rickmansworth.

The hind-end of a Hereford, built at Leysters Pole.

The fore-end of an Oxford, built at Kidlington.

10 Some examples of chamfering and wrought-iron work

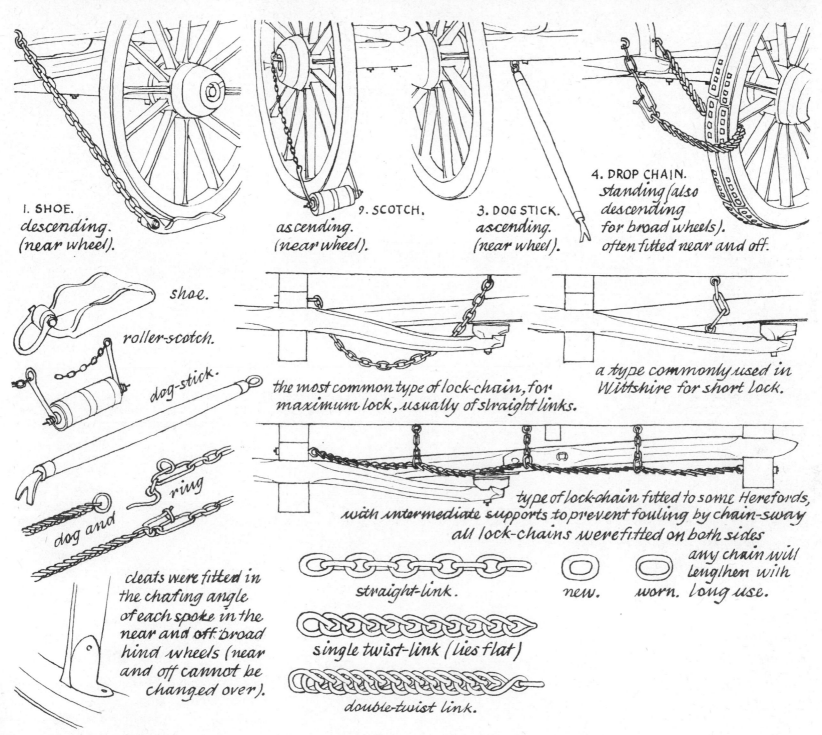

I. SHOE.
descending.
(near wheel).

9. SCOTCH.
ascending.
(near wheel).

3. DOG STICK.
ascending.
(near wheel).

4. DROP CHAIN.
standing (also
descending
for broad wheels).
often fitted near and off.

shoe.

roller-scotch.

dog-stick.

dog and *ring*

cleats were fitted in
the chafing angle
of each spoke in the
near and off broad
hind wheels (near
and off cannot be
changed over).

the most common type of lock-chain, for
maximum lock, usually of straight links.

a type commonly used in
Wiltshire for short lock.

type of lock-chain fitted to some Herefords,
with intermediate supports to prevent fouling by chain-sway
all lock-chains were fitted on both sides

straight-link.

new.

worn.

any chain will
lengthen with
long use.

single twist-link (lies flat)

double-twist link.

11 Types of brake and chain

hung from an adjacent hook. At the beginning of the descent the shoe was let down and let taut so that the wheel was carried on it, the taut shoe simply sliding down the hill. Only the near wheel was braked, the off keeping the waggon from sliding sideways. Such a shoe was necessarily very bulky and weighty, the more so for broad wheels, so that it was usual to wrap a long chain round the felloe of the broad wheel and secure it to the cross-piece. There were two lengths of chain; the longer, of double twist links, usually went round the wheel and was coupled to a sliding 'dog' or hook on a shorter length of straight-link chain attached together at the same point as shoes. It was usual to fit these 'drop chains' on both sides for alternate use. Wear on the wheels was reduced by fitting angle cleats where the chain passed round the felloes against the spokes, on one side only (a useful means of knowing an off wheel from a near wheel when both had been removed for greasing).

Brakes were not fitted to tip-carts, but the drop chain was so fitted to the various types of harvest-cart, gambo and wheelcar.

There were three kinds of chain. The straight oval link, and the twist and double twist, with each link turning a right angle so that the chain lay flat. The twist links were used to minimise chafing and were also used on the ridger chain on the shafts, over the harness pad.

Carrying the harvest
Various methods were employed, each of which tended to be peculiar to a region, but not invariably so. The most common was by adding frames, called ladders, to both front and back of the body of a waggon or cart. A ladder consisted of two side-pieces with two or three cross-pieces joining at the end, leaving the 'legs' free to be inserted into the body at the top or with a tail at floor-level. The sizes of ladders varied so much that one cannot give dimensions, but those used in Wiltshire were certainly the largest. Fore-ladders were usually placed at the top, either between the top- and out-raves or on or between the sides. In East Anglia they were often rested on the lower front-board with the top half removed.

A second type of frame was an 'all over', two-part frame, which was laid along the top of the body to meet midway. The harvest-frame was common in Lincolnshire and in Herefordshire, in which county the frame was called 'thripples'. The whole frame overlay the body considerably in both length and width and its capacity was considerable. In Herefordshire, ladders were often known as 'half-thripples'.

A third type consisted of a set of boards about 9in deep with pegs to fit between close-set out-raves and top. A variant of this was still deeper cratches, set all round for carrying sheep, etc. The boards were more commonly used in Hereford for conveying charcoal or coke.

A fourth type, commonly used in the Weald, on many Welsh carts and elsewhere rather locally, consisted of four ash poles, about 6ft in length, set at the corners of the body. In the Weald the whole load was finally secured by a long rope over the top from front to back where it was tightened on a rope roller, fitted under the hind cross-piece. Similar rollers, or windlasses, were to be found on waggons in Cornwall, where they were attached to the hind ladder. Some of the Hampshire waggons were so equipped.

For securing ropes on most waggons a set of hooks was fitted along each side, either fixed or swivelling on the outer rail, or like pig tails, and forged on to iron stays or standards.

Restricting lock by chains
Any fore-wheel that stands higher than the side member will make contact with that member at the maximum point of lock or turn unless restricted by means of chains on both sides. Most chains were fitted to run from the fore-bolster to a suitable point under the body, near the main cross-piece. At full lock the outer chain was pulled taut, keeping the inner wheel just clear of the side member, while the opposite chain hung loose. There were three systems of lock chain: (i) the most common, as described; (ii) a long chain each side from the fore-bolster to the hind-bed, suspended at three intermediate points by short chains to check undue swaying and prevent fouling; and (iii) a short chain each side, hanging vertically from the sides and secured to the hounds. The second type was commonly fitted to some Hereford waggons and the third to some of the Wessex waggons.

As any chain will wear by friction to the links and therefore lengthen in time, allowance had to be made when fitting. As a precaution it was the practice to fit iron plates or cleats to the sides where contact by the wheels would be made.

George Sturt in *The Wheelwright's Shop* estimated that about one-eighth of the original weight of wood in a waggon could safely be eliminated by careful shaving along exposed edges of the members between joints. This was known as chamfering and it produced a plain bevel along the edges (see Fig 10). In terms of function, it would not have been necessary to do more than this, but it was inevitable that wheelwrights should exercise their innate sense of a job worth doing well, by skilful use of the draw-knife. This developed to a remarkable degree in a number of regions, and was the case in the East Midlands, from Northants right up into Lincolnshire, and in the West of England, except Cornwall. Likewise in western Shropshire and in Herefordshire, at least on the early waggons. Even when the panel-sided designs gave place to the simpler plank-bodied waggons, the undercarriages continued to have the most elaborate chamfering.

In nearly every case a waggon carried the owner's name and that of the farm, with the county, on the headboard. In the West of England the maker's name usually was put on the tail-board. In addition the name and farm appeared on the off-side of the body at the fore-end. In the eastern half of England this was written in white on a rectangular black iron plate. In Gloucestershire, west of the Cotswolds, and in the Marches, the name and farm appeared on a long wooden strip below the top-rail. The Oxford waggons had the particulars written directly on the panel boards. There were, of course, various forms in many other regions. In the Weald, where most waggons had spars or spindles on the head-board, there was only rarely any branding and the only identity was on the iron plate. The waggons of Northamptonshire and Holland were notable for the elaborate display of the names of both the owner and the maker.

In considering the merits of all the designs in their variant forms, the amateur is likely to judge on appearances. Such a judgement will quite reasonably derive from an idea of what constitutes a good-looking vehicle and may hardly be concerned with the use of a vehicle in the daily round of the farm. But as show judges considered the points of a good horse, so those who used waggons knew what to look for.

It is known among people who have been acquainted with farm vehicles that there were those designs which gave a good average performance, that there were certain designs which were as excellent as the reputations of their makers, and that there were others that had some defect in use, such as a floor pitched too high or a structural weakness. Some had vital parts too frail; others were unnecessarily strong and therefore unduly heavy. Some were heavy in draught. If the wheels had too little foreway or 'gather', they ran hard on the noses of their axle-arms. A waggon with a near-side wheelbase slightly longer than the off would continually run out of course. Even more important was that all four wheels had a uniform dish and all axle-arms a uniform cant. J. P. Bingham, in a letter to the writer, remarked:

> The front and rear carriages also had to be true and square, because when fitting up the axles the 'line up' of the wheels was taken from the sides of the main frame. Also, when lining up the shafts this was done by taking a line from the centre of the hind-buck (cross-piece) over the centre of the nose-piece and right through to the centre of the front end of the shafts. For the four wheels to be correct they each had to run inwards by $\frac{3}{16}$in (like a pin-toed person) so that the wheels pressed a little on the shoulders of the axle-arms and not on the end collars. The waggon would then run as easily as a railway wagon when once started.

It is worth noting that the best waggons were always made 'one by one' from start to finish with each part made to fit the next. Any repetitive process in which each part was made in a batch resulted in vehicles incomparable with the 'one by one'. Mass-production will never be equated with quality. Quotations of prices to cover all regions over 150 years would make tedious reading out of context with the present book, but an indication of the decline and rise consequent upon political events may be had by quoting Sussex waggons at £80 each in 1780–90 against £30 in 1870. Waggons made in the Holland part of Lincolnshire cost £35 in 1903 and tip-carts in 1945 cost £125. Prices now being paid by collectors are purely artificial at £100 plus since the same waggon could have been bought at a sale in 1946 for ten shillings. The record to date, for an old waggon, is £250. There must have been some hot bidding.

3 From the Ox to the Horse

In the days of the long-distance road carriers, teams of four, six or eight oxen were yoked in pairs by trace-chains to a centre draught-pole on the fore-carriage. When horses took their place similar teams were used but with two pairs of shafts taking the place of the pole.

Where oxen continued to be used it was usual, on the Cotswolds and in Wiltshire, to harness the oxen in collars instead of the yoke and in some cases shafts were used; elsewhere, as in Sussex, the yoke was used with chains. This was usually made of hornbeam and was secured by ash bows to the necks of the animals and coupled in the centre to the chains or the pole. The 'master' ox was on the fore off side and when an inexperienced pair were being trained they were placed between the leaders and the pole or shaft pair.

The continued use of oxen to a late date in some regions may occasion surprise, but the ox was easier to train and less fastidious in its feed than the horse; also, while a horse would sometimes 'give up' in extreme difficulties, the ox would still plod on, step by step. The breeds most commonly used were the Sussex Red, the Welsh Black, the Old Gloucester, the Hereford, and a cross between the Red Gloucester and the Hereford. In East Anglia the Devon was favoured.

For shoeing the cloven hoof, cues, in two pieces, were secured by five nails on the outside and four on the inside (see Fig 12). An ox could not be trained to lift its hoof for cueing, as a horse can, and the animal had to be thrown on deep grass. It went down quite gently, while a boy sat on its neck. The four hooves were tied to a wooden tripod. The farrier would use a large lump of pork fat as a 'pin cushion' for the nails; this also greased the nails so that they went into the hooves more easily. When the ox was released, it rose to its feet, gave a mighty shake and resumed grazing. Some animals had to be muzzled to prevent them from grazing when working in trace.

The change from ox to horse was a very long one and was extremely irregular, from the eastern half of England to the western parts and Wales. The first known use of the horse in draught was in East Anglia during the twelfth century, but it was not until armour was rendered out of date by musketry and cannon that the real change began. The war horses of former battles, the coursers, then became available for work on farm and road. Later, there came the enclosures, dividing the old fields into smaller units of about ten acres, each group worked by one man, two horses and a modified plough.

By the eighteenth century better characteristics were being bred into the draught horses, concurrent with improvements in cattle and sheep. The heaviest horses were for the plough and the waggon, the medium for the coach and the lighter and smaller for the hill farms. In Suffolk the Punch became established in 1813, and the Clydesdale in Scotland in 1830, and rather later, in 1875, the Shire of the Midlands. The smallest breeds, such as the Welsh Cob, stemmed from the pack horse. The 'feathering' on the legs of the Clydesdale and the Shire was bred as a fashion down to about 1900 or later, but long before then the short-limbed Punch had been bred clean of limb, being less prone to what was known as 'blemish'.

The day's work began and ended much earlier than now, with

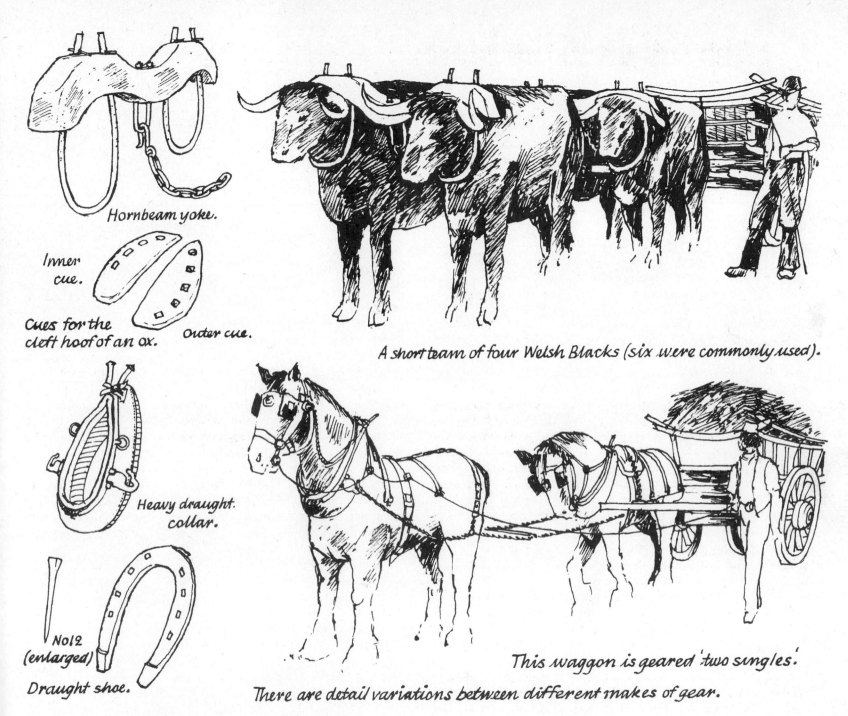

Hornbeam yoke.

Inner cue.

Cues for the cleft hoof of an ox.

Outer cue.

A short team of four Welsh Blacks (six were commonly used).

Heavy draught collar.

No12 (enlarged)

Draught shoe.

This waggon is geared 'two singles'.

There are detail variations between different makes of gear.

12 Some details of shoes and harness used in draught work

no field work on Sundays. The carters and horsemen were up very early to bait the horses and give them two hours to digest their feed before starting work. After a morning's work the horses were uncoupled during the meal break and then recoupled to finish during the afternoon. With a team of oxen at the plough, it was usual to work through to a finish, earlier in the afternoon, before unyoking. The animals were left in field or stable to graze, feed or sleep at will.

Harnessing a horse to a waggon or cart was known as 'shutting in' and the reverse of this operation was 'shutting out'. It was a single-handed task in which the horse was walked back between the shafts as they rested on the ground. Carts, however, were stored with their shafts suspended from the shed roof, from which they were lowered when the horse was in position.

Shutting in was begun on the off side. The tug-chain, from the collar, was coupled to the long staple on the shaft blade, taking the weight and leaving the man free to complete the task. The ridge-chain was thrown over the back-pad and the breech-chain coupled. The man then went round to the near-side where the loose end of the ridge-chain was hooked to the staple. The tug- and breech-chains were then coupled up.

When 'shutting out' a horse, a different reverse order was followed. (1, off-side breech; 2, off-side tug; 3, near-side breech; 4, near-side tug; 5, ridge-chain uncoupled and thrown over; 6, shafts lowered to ground.) The three sets of chains served the following purposes; the ridge took the weight of the shafts on the back-pad. The horse pulled by the tug-chains and was backed against the breech-chains. If a second or additional horses were necessary, they were harnessed by trace-chains and wore a different harness which had no back-pad. A slim pole, called a spreader, between opposite traces kept them from swaying.

Working practice varied from one region to another. Although shafts were generally adopted, Yorkshire, among several regions, used the centre draught-pole until quite late. For pair-horse working, some regions used two pairs of shafts, though most had the horses harnessed tandem-wise. In Herefordshire, for example, horses were geared 'three singles' and in Suffolk 'three at length' (the same thing). Very often the leading rein was the property of the carter. It is an interesting but incidental point that while in some counties the carter would ride a light horse side-saddle back to the stable, this was frowned upon in other counties, such as Herefordshire.

Some notes on the collar and harness will be in place here. The collar was made of leather and stuffed with either straw or flock and the inner surface was faced with either serge or flannel. The hames, at first of wood but later of brass, fitted a groove in

Map 1 The waggon zone, showing the distribution of types and designs. Designs shown thus – COTSWOLD. Continuous arrows indicate areas of influences; broken arrows slight influences. Boundaries can only be approximate as intrusions occurred everywhere. Distribution of late designs, eg Boat and Barge, depend upon sales, but places of manufacture are shown where space permits

MOORS

YORKSHIRE
GROUP

WOLDS

DALES

• Beverley

Industry

Industry

North limit of Lock-arch

West limit of Lock-arch

• Lincoln

LINCOLNSHIRE

Dairy

DERBYSHIRE

CROOKED BED

STAFFORDSHIRE

H E R M A P H R O D I T E

Fen

NORFOLK
GROUP

Snowdon

DENBIGHSHIRE

Moor

Moor

Dairy

Industry

West limit of Lock-arch

EAST MIDLAND
'DISC'

• Rothwell

Fen

EAST ANGLIAN GROUP

SUFFOLK GROUP

Moor

MONTGOMERY

CORVEDALE

CLUN

RADNOR TROLLEY

HEREFORD
GROUP

Malverns

WORCESTER

• Bromsgrove

EAST MIDLAND
'WHEATSHEAF'

• Northampton

OUSE
'SPECTACLE'

• Long Melford

CROPREDY

• Banbury

East limit of Bow-wave

CAMBRIDGE

ESSEX
GROUP

Moor

BRECON
Mountains

MON-
MOUTH

NORTH GLOSTER

Gloster

COTSWOLD

CROOKED BED

VALE OF
AYLESBURY

VALE OF
WHITEHORSE

CROOKED BED

WAIST BED

HERTFORDSHIRE

SOUTH-
MINSTER

Industry

GLAMORGAN

SOUTH
GLOSTER

WILTSHIRE

North limit of Straight-bed

Urban/Industry *Market Gardens*

South limit of
Loch-arch

East limit of Cock-wave

• Andover

East limit of Bow-wave

Urban/Industry North limit of Waist-bed

SURREY
• Farnham

KENT
• Ashford

Moor

SOMERSET

Dulverton

WEST OF ENGLAND
GROUP

DEVON

Thorverton

DORSET

Forest

HAMPSHIRE

Boundary between Straight and Waist-bed

WEALDEN GROUP

SUSSEX

West limit of Cock-wave

Moor

• Exmouth

CORNWALL

Moor

33

the collar next the wall on the fore-edge. The hames were in two pieces coupled by rings at the bottom and secured by straps at the top. The tug-hooks were hinged to the hames. The ridge-pad was made in a similar way to the collar, but on a foundation of beech called a 'tree'. Along the spine of the horse lay meeter straps which joined collar, pad and crupper-strap, and from the latter hung straps to carry the heavy, broad breech-strap. The pad was adjusted by a girth strap or straps. There were also straps which carried the familiar brasses, a short one at the forehead and a long one from the collar to the girth. Upon the saddler's skill depended the satisfactory working of the horses. Carters knew the size of a farm by the number of horses used there.

Some mention should be made of the brasses. In the earliest times they served as amulets against the forces of darkness and their designs were derived from such motifs as the crescent. As time went on, the original idea became lost amid a growing variety of motifs commemorating historical events, jubilees and awards at shows. At one time the carrier's team carried a set of bells which gave warning of approach. All brasses, the trees of saddles, the metal parts and the saddlers' tools were made chiefly at Walsall.

Both the draught-shoe and the lighter one for riding were a long time evolving to the patterns we know today. At the Curtiss Museum in Alton, Hampshire, we may see examples of typical shoes of each period dating back to Romano-Celtic times, and note the features of each period. Much depended on the development of the anvil. Little could be achieved until the beak and wedge were added to the anvil. The Celtic shoes had deep and wide countersinking about each nail hole, each with a pronounced bulge, which was eliminated by the eleventh century. The shoe, however, became asymmetrical with a broad surface on the outer side. The calkin on the Celtic shoe disappeared on the inner side and was made shallower on the outer tip. The tread of the shoe became broader with a groove along the line of the nails during the seventeenth and eighteenth centuries, and during the latter century acquired the 'keyhole' which was soon eliminated. It was not until the nineteenth century that both shoes reached their final forms, the draught-shoe tapering gently in tread from the nose to the points with a calkin on the outer point only and a raised clip on the nose to fit against the hoof for stability. By this time the riding-shoe had a continuous groove.

A draught-shoe weighed about $1\frac{1}{2}$lb and had four nail holes on each side. The nails were number twelves, which were about 3in long and had wedged heads to bed in the countersunk holes. When a horse was taken to the farrier for its first shoeing it was not its first visit—that was made in the company of another horse so that it might become accustomed to the farriery. Once the horse and the farrier became acquainted the next visit for shoeing was made much easier. The farrier had to be a vet as well and to love horses, and had to be able to rectify peculiarities in any horse. A horse worked solely on the land required shoeing every three months, but one worked on the roads, metalled or otherwise, might have to be reshod every three or four weeks.

The attention paid to waggons at harvest home was equalled by that given to the horses and the harness. Even a journey to market required that every strap be well rubbed up and every brass polished.

4 Regional Design

The Weald

One never saw many waggons up on the Downs between Beachy Head and Harting. They were all about the farms down on the levels and in the undulating country that was once all Wealden Forest. They were there in their threes, fours and more, even in the dry coombs that thread among the Downs on the coastward side.

At one time the Downland of Sussex was all sheep. Sheep, dew-ponds, a lonely shepherd and endless windy, thyme-scented miles of short, fine turf and a sou'west wind that sometimes carried salt spray for miles. Southdown sheep were biggish animals that gave the finest mutton one could wish for. It was like that when I was a boy spending my summer holidays with Grandfather.

Since the last war, people have stopped eating mutton and too many of those glorious miles have gone under the plough. Some-times I think of Belloc and could wish that a few men who were boys when I was could stand and gaze across the lazy convulsions of the tidal Ouse, where still veers the gilded dolphin of Kipling's windy Piddinghoe. And when we'd had our fill we would hike the long miles back to the Eight Bells at Jevington and call for some Sussex bitter. Some say you can't do that now.

The waggons of Kent and Sussex were all built with waist-bed bodies, and in place of the usual tail-board nearly every waggon had a wooden bar, called a hawk, which fitted into slots at each corner and the load was secured by a long rope passed over the top from the front, to be wound tight on a rope roller. They also differed in having the fore and main transverse members morticed to the side pieces on the same plane.

Most of the waggons had a lidded box for spare links, etc, on the front in Kent and the near-side in Sussex, with the usual exceptions. Some of the Kentish waggons had oil-axles but none was noted in Sussex, where a few had wooden arms. The wheel diameters were fairly uniform, 48in for the fore-wheels and 56–58in for the hind. The fore-wheels had twelve spokes and the hind fourteen, except in West Sussex where ten and twelve were more common. While the majority of Sussex waggons had a 4in tread, almost half the Kents had 3½in treads with rather fewer at 4in.

The body of a typical Kent waggon had straight iron N-standards and wooden crooks, but in Sussex the standards were curved, cyma-fashion, and in most cases, particularly in the west, the remaining supports were iron 'cupid's bows'. In order to get the curve in the fore-panel, they used poplar instead of elm. The great majority had closed raves set rather steeply, but many in West Sussex had open double out-raves. Whereas every Sussex waggon had a blue body, seventy-five per cent of Kent waggons had a colour variously described as stone or cream with the remainder in blue. Scarlet was usual for the undercarriage in Kent, but in Sussex this was usually painted red oxide.

There was a difference in the sheer of the body. In the Sussex waggons there was a continuous easy curve, but the Kentish had a straight rise fore and aft from the main standard. The two counties differed on yet another detail, the Kent waggon having eleven to thirteen flat spars each side, set vertically or nearly so, but most Sussex waggons had sixteen or more spindles with a slight rake to fore and aft. The majority of the Sussex waggons had mid-raves and spindles on sides and head, but some in West Sussex had plain

13 **Kent:** Built by Holt of Staplehurst. Body buff, undercarriage red. No identity. Noted at Staplehurst

head-panels painted red and bearing the owner's identity. Otherwise, this lack of identity on the head-board was typical of the region. Nothing more than the black rectangular plate at the fore off end, in Sussex, and usually in Kent, black lettering symmetrically on the off-rave above the main standard. Heathfield's waggons were so branded but Pope had his name incised on the oil-axle caps. Nearly every waggon had the body permanently attached to the hind-carriage, dispensing with pole spreaders and the hind bolster, with wood blocks taking their place. There is substantial evidence that well into the nineteenth century the waggons of the Weald were built open-sided without panel boards. I noted such a waggon at Amberley in 1940 and in the Weald and Downland Museum at Singleton they have a 'hop waggon', once owned by Whitbread, that had panels at the lower half of the tail end. This has steeply set ladders. The waggons that were familiar enough in East Sussex were less common in West Sussex where the designs of Hampshire and West Surrey intruded deeply. It could be confusing to the recorder, especially if a waggon which was 'not quite Kent' was also present, as at Shipley.

A list issued by Heathfield & Sons, of Ashford, showed that their waggons were built in six sizes, from 30cwt on 2in wheels to 5 tons on 4½in wheels. The larger sizes could be fitted with double shafts if required. Heathfield's waggons had the main-pin inverted

with a large hook at the bottom, the purpose not known. In Sussex it was usual to gear extra horses singly, in line.

Two waggons noted at Doddington, between Faversham and Harrietsham, deviated from 'county' practice in having mid-raves and spars on head and sides, and painted blue. Otherwise they conformed, with attached bodies and 3½in wheels. Both were made by Humphries of Doddington for T. Barr of Paden Street (see Fig 14). Waggons made by Heathfield of Ashford, Pope of Chidding-stone and Holt of Staplehurst were similar, but Richard Walker, a model maker, found a waggon at Naxted Farm, near Lyminge, which had quarter-round fore corners to the body frame instead of the square angle. The waggon must have been a real veteran because it had broad wheels, which are almost unknown in Kent.

A waggon which was branded 'W. Boniface. 1888 West Grinstead' was noted in 1949 on Needs Farm near Partridge Green. It was something of a hybrid with attached body, red-panelled head and double out-raves. This, too, was quite old, with broad, straked wheels hung on wooden arms.

George D. Woolgar, of East Grinstead, built a nice waggon for the Wiston Estate, at Steyning, which I noted in 1947. The body was spindled all round, nineteen on each side and six on the head, with panel boards laced. But the 4in wheels were all spoked four-teen and afforded interesting comparison with a Gloucester noted

14 **Kent:** Built by Humphries of Doddington. Body blue, undercarriage red. Noted at Doddington

15 **Sussex:** Builder not known. Body blue, undercarriage Venetian red. Noted at Ketches Farm, Sheffield Green

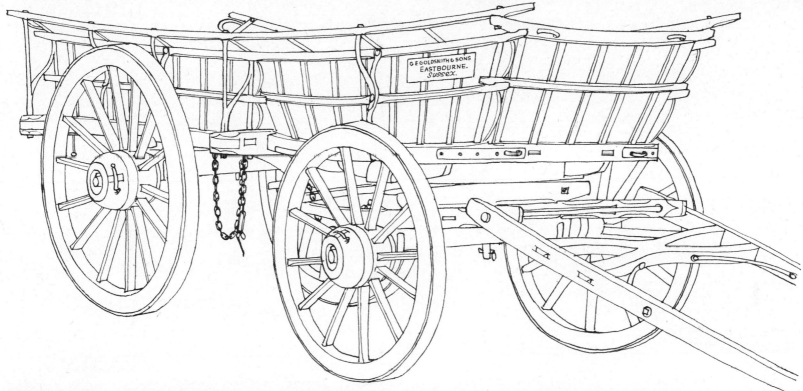

16 Sussex: Builder not known. Body blue, undercarriage Venetian red. Noted on Crapham Down, near Beachy Head

near Bishops Cleeve in 1964. This had ten spokes all round. The Wiston waggon was equipped with a tail-board.

Throughout the Weald there was a marked absence of elaboration and the chamfering was usually quite elementary. The waggons tended to look austere but they were very well designed and thoroughly practical. The comparative uniformity of the two designs was in striking contrast with certain other regions. For purposes of immediate comparison, the Kent and Sussex designs have been set out in Table 3.

Table 3 Comparison of Kent and Sussex waggons

		Kent	Sussex
Totals recorded in each county		82	56
		(percentages)	
Wheel treads (inches)	2½	10	9
	3	—	4
	3½	49	14
	4	41	64
	6	1	9
Spoking fore/aft	12/14	100	68
	10/12	—	32
Located in:	Kent	78	—
	East Sussex	13	80
	West Sussex	—	17
	Surrey	9	3
Fore-summers	1	95	13
	2	5	87
Mid-rail present		3½	100
Intermediate supports	wood	94	34
	iron	6	66
Colour of body	cream/stone	75	—
	blue	25	100

(Additional evidence could alter the percentages)

17 **Sussex:** Built by George Woolgar of East Grinstead. Body blue, undercarriage Venetian red. Noted on Wiston Estate, Steyning

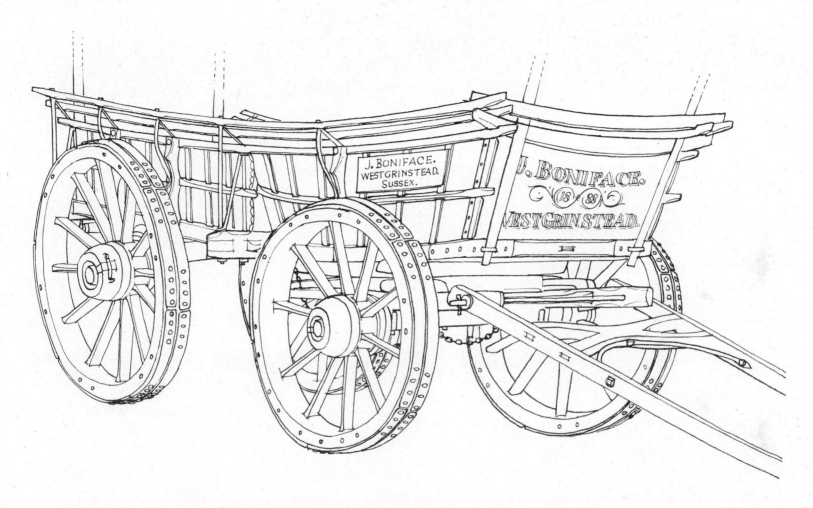

18 Sussex: Builder not known—c1850. Wooden axle-trees. Body blue,
undercarriage Venetian red. Head-board red

19 **Surrey:** Built by S. Horder & Sons of Loxwood, Sussex. Body blue, with red head-board; undercarriage red. No identity

Hampshire and West Surrey

It could be said that the designs of this region had a West of England orientation which made them quite different from those of Sussex. The political boundary of Hampshire was intruded upon by Dorset influence to the north of the New Forest and by Wiltshire toward Whitchurch. There was a similar Berkshire intrusion toward Basingstoke from the Kennet valley and the distant Vale of the White Horse. Hampshire and West Surrey in turn obtruded in West Sussex.

During the nineteenth century, London was rapidly over-running Surrey, leaving a rural strip along the south and west. Although much of the whole region is agricultural in land usage, the urban development is considerable and in terms of farming there are several areas which cannot be rendered productive. There is what the geologists term the Bagshot Bed (and which Cobbett called a 'rascally heath'). Between Southampton and Portsmouth there is a conurbation and to the west lies the New Forest. Altogether, these areas account for a considerable proportion of the whole region. The farming areas are divisible into cereal and dairy-farming, so that the overall demand for harvest-waggons cannot at any time have been very great. It is all the more gratifying therefore to find that the waggons made were in no way inferior in design. There

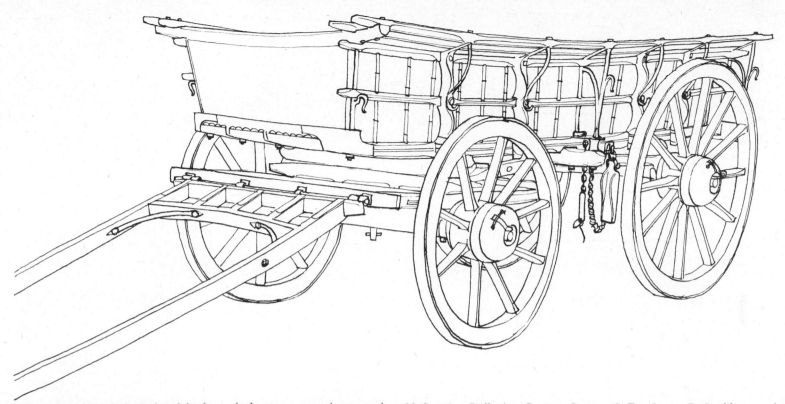

were no waggons with waisted beds and the two counties consti-
tuted an eastern extension of a large region where the straight-bed
waggons were universal. Notable among the wheelwrights were
Etheridge of Bishops Waltham; Hetherington of Alton; Elliot and
Sturt, both of Farnham, and Horder of Loxwood, just in Sussex.

Hetherington's waggons had four summers, middle-raves and
spindled sides with double out-raves supported by iron N-standards
and a pair of iron cupid's bows above each axle line. The flat iron
running-pins at the fore-ends were cranked to enter the side frame
behind the front piece, a feature copied by Elliot who otherwise
followed Sturt (or perhaps Sturt followed Elliot). Most of Hetherington's waggons had twenty spindles on each side and a shallow
waggon-box between the near-side front cupid's bows and above
the mid-rave. The fore-ends of the protruding panel boards were
very nicely chamfered. The head panel was plain and was topped
by a stout concave rail. The panelled tail-board had a convex rail
and was barrel-hinged. Ladders were fitted to lie flat, the fore at
rail height and the tail at floor level, and the latter had a rope
roller under its extremity.

Hetherington made two waggons for William Brock of Manor
Farm, West Worldham. The fore-carriage had turntable rings and
four hounds with a splinter-bar head, but a third waggon, possibly

20 **Surrey:** Built by George Sturt, of Farnham. Body blue, undercarriage red, head-board red. Noted at Selborne, Hampshire

21 **Hampshire:** Built by Hetherington & Co Ltd, of Alton. Body ochre, undercarriage red, head-board red

made by Elliot for Mrs B. E. Cook of Bennet Hill, Wonersh (near Guildford), had the shafts draught-pinned to two hounds. A fourth, made for W. J. and T. L. Hayden of Lode Farm, Kingsley, had the splinter-bar, but exceptionally had a crooked bed; and all of these waggons could be identified by pole braces made of curved iron bars instead of wood and usually by the cast-iron maker's plate at the bottom fore-edge of the near side. They all ran on 3in wheels with twelve spokes in the fore and fourteen in the hind. The bodies were painted an ochreous buff, lined pale blue on chamfer edges. The undercarriages were scarlet, lined out in black. The waggons were fully braked, with a dog stick for the trailing brake. Mrs Cook's waggon was exceptional in having the raves closed instead of double. One of Mr Brock's waggons had twelve spokes all round, but all had fore-wheels 42in in diameter and 56in for the hind. On a red head-panel the branding was in black sans-serif letters, shaded pale blue.

The waggons made by Etheridge were not dissimilar except that

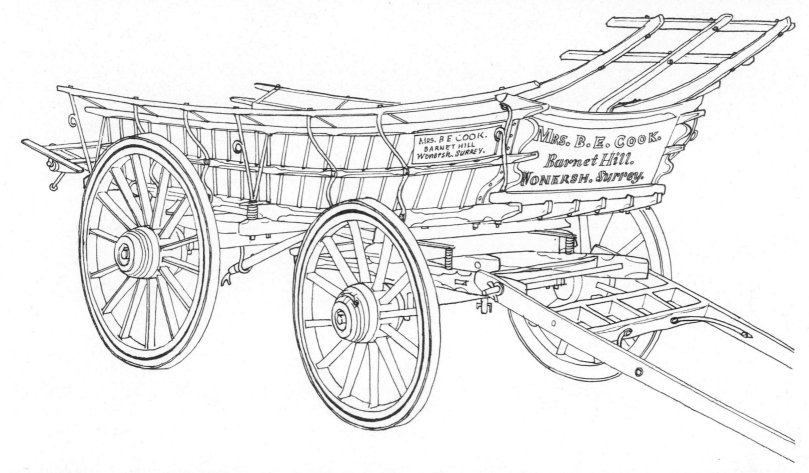

the head-board was set plank fashion athwart the sides in the Dorset manner. This plank had bold cyma curved sides flaring out to the extreme width over the raves. The whole body had the same gentle sheer, but ran on 3in wheels, spoked ten in fore and twelve in hind.

In the Curtiss Museum at Alton there is a model on the scale of 1:8 by Waiting that is worth close examination. It closely resembles the waggons of Berkshire, with a waisted bed and full-bow *treble* raves. In place of spindles there were seventeen flat spars and the ladders, though large, were curved to terminate vertically. The sides were supported by iron standards and the plank tailboard had pin and eye hinges. A single pair of shafts was hinged by splinter-bar to four hounds. Both the body and the ladders were painted yellow, with a red undercarriage, and the waggon ran on large, narrow wheels, fairly dished. A photograph, taken by Waiting at Monk Sherborne, north of Basingstoke, showed a similar waggon, which differed in having double raves and a

22 **Hampshire:** Built by Elliott of Farnham. Body ochre, lined out in blue. Undercarriage red, lined out in black. Head-board red

23 **Dorset:** Built by Forsey of Symondsbury, Bridport. Body blue, head-board yellow, undercarriage orange. A small waggon, with a 114in body, 40in fore-wheels and 50in hind-wheels

crooked bed about 5½in deep. The iron standard hinted at Wilt-shire rather than Berkshire, having a very curved Y.

When one has read time and again *The Wheelwright's Shop* by George Sturt, his name tends to become synonymous with Surrey, even though Farnham is more Hampshire in character. Waiting himself appeared to doubt if there ever was a Surrey waggon and I find myself in some agreement. Although most, but not all, of Sturt's waggons had blue bodies, the affinity with Alton is obvious and Elliott, who made waggons close by in West Street, followed Alton as described above, finishing his vehicles in the Alton buff.

The Sturt waggons had a distinctive shape to the N-standards and had double out-raves and about seventeen spindles and a middle-rave. Above each axle there were two wooden supports and a conspicuous feature was the red head-panel which was set flush with the side panels. Most had a splinter-bar on four hounds but there were exceptions. Sturt made his wheels rather larger than most, at 50in and 62in with 3in treads and spoked ten and twelve. Such was a waggon made for Henry Lunn of Elvetham, Hampshire.

There were variations, as usual, and a waggon made for Alfred Karn of Somerset Farm, Thursley, had a yellow body (which had badly faded when I knew it during the middle fifties). There were thirteen spindles and one iron stay above each axle. The wheels were spoked twelve all round and the shafts were draught-pinned. Another, near Selborne, conformed to a Sturt waggon in every feature.

S. Horder & Sons, of Loxwood, Sussex, followed Sturt rather than their Sussex neighbours. The bodies were a little deeper, retaining the mid-raves but with only twelve spindles. The N-standards were quite straight and there was one wooden support above each axle and there was a rope roller under the hind piece. The head-board was plain, but the tail was panelled, with barrel hinges. The shafts were set *between* the hounds. A Horder waggon

24 **Dorset:** Built by Forsey of Symondsbury, Bridport, for Joseph Gibbs of Moorbath, Symondsbury. Body blue, with yellow panels. Undercarriage orange

noted at Ewhurst had a blue body and the white oval maker's plate on the near-side. Another waggon, branded 'G 1910 C', belonged to George Cole of Lurgashall, between Haslemere and Petworth. It was generally in conformity, with a rope roller and the normal draught-pinned shafts. The iron sockets to take corner poles showed some influence from East Sussex. The ciphers 'G 1910 C' were in bold seriffed characters in yellow, shaded blue on a red panel enclosed by blue. A yellow border had reversed radii corners. These waggons were not numerous, but one encountered them in many unexpected places. Sometimes it was not easy or even possible to identify their makers, but they were all of interest.

West of England

The West of England, consisting of Dorset, Somerset, Devon and Cornwall, part Saxon, part Celtic, not a little of high moorland and some of it fenland, with the greater part limestone, millstone and chalk, cannot be dealt with neatly. In culture and topography it is remarkably diverse so it comes as a surprise to find that east of the Tamar there was originally only one basic design of waggon. That design underwent only one significant change, late in the nineteenth century, which design, at least in the eastern half of the region, survived into quite recent times. It was in the Exe Valley, between Tiverton and Exmouth, and at Bridgwater and Bagborough near Crowcombe that a major break with tradition occurred after the 1850s.

The relationship between topography, land-usage and waggon design is a subject in itself for rewarding study. In East Anglia, for example, we find the situation reversed with a dozen or more variants of at least five designs distributed over a region that is fairly uniform in topography and land-usage. West of the Tamar, waggons were never numerous and were nearly all derived from

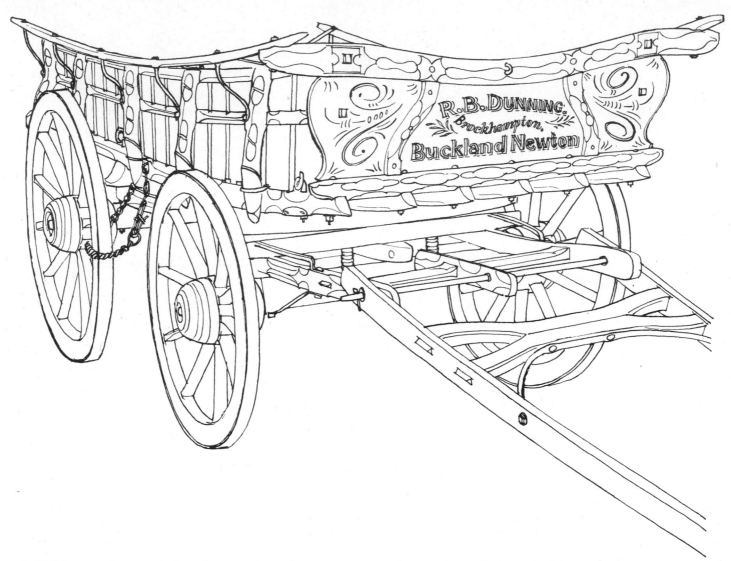

25 **Dorset:** Builder not known. Body yellow, undercarriage orange. Centre head-panel red

the Cornish wain. The design had a low-sided, almost platform body, and ran on small wheels providing a full lock. This vehicle was well suited to the winding lanes and light crops. Surprisingly, Cornwall did not heed either Wales or Brittany. Here and there one might be lucky and find a 'chest' waggon which more closely resembled English designs (see Fig 33).

The basic design of the three English counties was elaborately made, with distinctive bow-raves and panelled sides on a straight bed. The fore-end rose quite sharply and the hind-bows turned up

at the rear instead of running down to the floor level. Irrespective of builder or locality, all these waggons had these features in common. The head- and tail-boards were identical and set athwart the sides, which had middle-raves, double out-raves and were supported by well-chamfered wooden standards which were usually clasped by iron sockets. All the body frames had four summers and with no known exception, the wheels were spoked ten in fore and twelve in hind. Their diameters were appreciably smaller than average, making the waggons appear even smaller than they were. Anyone accustomed to look up to the large waggons of other regions could experience a mild shock on a first encounter in the west. These waggons were all painted blue with branding in several

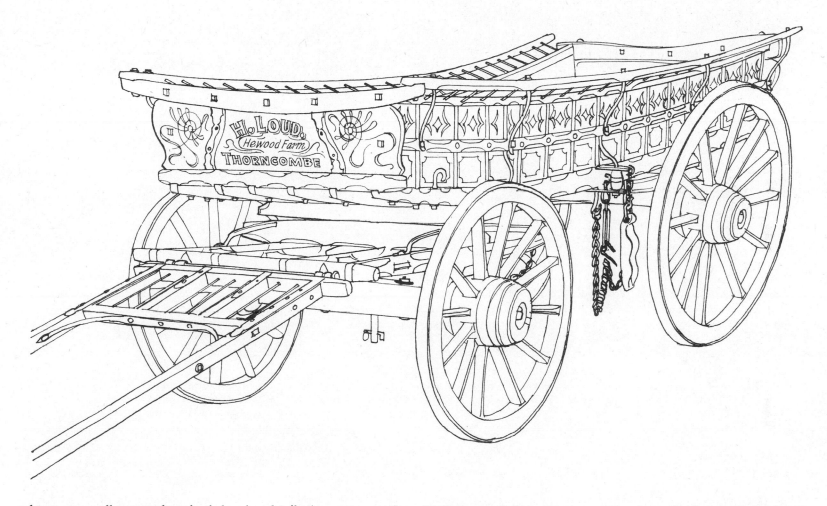

colours on a yellow panel on both head and tail, the owner on the head and builder with painting date on the tail, but there were exceptions. The undercarriages were scarlet. Each side had about twelve spars set more or less vertically, but many of the Devon waggons had seventeen or eighteen spindles set raked to fore and aft of the centre. The use of square iron continued longer than in other regions, so the spiral in the ironwork was always to be noticed. Very few of these waggons had projecting main-beams; mostly they were flush with the sides. No example of closed raves is known to the writer.

During the late nineteenth century a slow change occurred in which the bow was dispensed with by deepening the body enough

26 **Somerset:** Built by Rossiter of Crewkerne in 1910. Body black, with yellow centre-panel. Side-panels have yellow flowers and red panels. Undercarriage orange

to allow the raves to run in a sheer from front to back. The shafts were generally, but not always, draught-pinned to two hounds. The wheels were mostly dished shallowly, though in Devon they were a little deeper. Nearly all had 3in treads, hooped, though one could find 5in wheels here and there. No broad wheels were known to have been built after 1850. Most waggons were fully braked, with drop chain, shoe and scotch.

The head- and tail-rails were all fairly deep in proportion to the

49

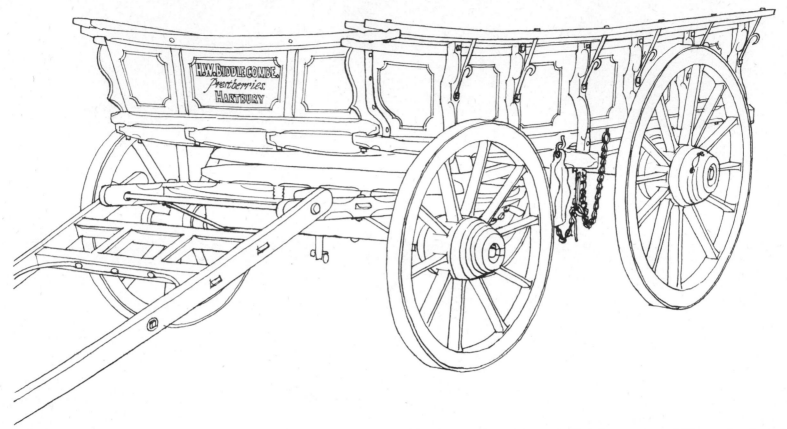

27 **Somerset:** A break with tradition by Cummins of Bridgwater. Body blue, panel-lined in white; undercarriage red. Prestberries Farm is seven miles north of Gloucester

height of the boards and slightly concave between level ends, except in Devon where they were straight. The waggons of the three counties could be distinguished one from another by subtle differences in the lettering styles and the ornamental brushwork. The bow over the hind-wheel was generally known as a cock-rave. I am informed by R. H. Alford of Exeter that the term 'ship-waggon' was understood only in East Devon. Elsewhere in the county the term was not recognised. Concurrently with the elimination of the cock-rave a few builders, mainly in Dorset, began setting the head- and tail-boards between the sides.

The winds of change must have been blowing strongly during the 1840s and 1850s. It was Alford who passed on to me the information given by a Devon wheelwright that during the repeal of the corn laws, those farmers in favour had their waggons re-painted yellow, while the 'opposition' remained blue. I have inquired without success and it does seem unlikely that any farmer would risk the wrath of his neighbours by exhibiting his views. Rick-burning and sheep-worrying still have enough causes. A more likely explanation is that the change in colour was one of many taking place. Millers have for long been partial to yellow waggons.

28 **Somerset:** Built by Ridge & Son, of North Petherton, Bridgwater. Body blue, lined out in white; undercarriage orange. Date shows last painting. Note half-panelled body and straked narrow wheels

Far more important were the Bath and West Shows in 1852, 53, 54 and 55, when George Milford took 'firsts' for his new waggons. They were a clean break with tradition, having simple plank-sided bodies with no frills. There was some quality in the making that enabled them to run well. The break was emphasised by a colour change, from blue to ochre. Since then other makers have followed suit, in this change, though some of them, such as Cummins of Bridgwater and Gill of Exmouth, remained faithful to blue. Gill made a beauty for T. Dance & Son, then farming near Exmouth, but later moving to Marden, Herefordshire. This waggon was remarkable for the painstaking work which had been put into a waggon so lately built. The body was blue, panel-lined in white, and the white undercarriage was lined out in black. The lettering on the head panel could not be faulted, as could so much contemporary 'writing' (as it was termed). Cummins, whose firm had built cock-raved waggons on 5in wheels, made a panel-lined waggon for H. W. Biddlecomb of Prestberries Farm, Hartbury, Glos (see Fig 27), and Woollen of Bagborough, near Crowcombe, made one for R. F. Bond of Kingston nearby. Pike of Whitestone followed Milford of Thorverton in his design. James White of

29 **Devon:** Built by Gill of Exmouth. Repainted c1930 by a Leominster 'writer'. Body blue, lined out in white; undercarriage white, lined out in black

Tedburn St Mary had at least one by Pike, in ochre and red. In 1910 Rossiter, who had served his apprenticeship under Vincent of Ham and then set up at Crewkerne, commemorated the Coronation with a waggon for Henry Loud of Thorcombe. The body was *black* with a scarlet interior, and was elaborately panelled in scarlet, with floral motifs in yellow. The whole effect in a drawing is remarkable enough, but on the day the waggon came out of the paint-shop, passers-by must have been fairly dazzled (see Fig 26).

The peak in waggon activity and traditional design may be dated c 1875, after which came the decline resulting from events in history. Some of the most satisfying waggons, aesthetically, were

made in the seventies. Richards of Stoborough, near Wareham; Kail of Horton, near Cranborne; and Kiddle of East Stour were all active then. The finish on their woodwork was not so much chamfering as woodcarving. The time when such work would be derided was far ahead.

Cummins made several waggons for A. Edwards of Boundary Farm, Glastonbury. When I saw one such waggon in 1950 it had been last painted in 1913 and was wearing well. Where the wheel-wrights in some regions were adopting straight lines and minimal chamfering, the men of the west continued the cyma curves and detail elaboration. The tongue-pole of Cummins' waggon had two

30 **Devon:** Built by Milford of Thorverton in 1887. Body ochre, under-carriage red

31 **Devon:** Built by Langford of Northleigh, Barnstaple, in 1867. Body blue, with yellow panel; undercarriage red. Note the raked verticals and the straight head-rail

cyma curves between the fore-bolster and the hind-beam and the four hounds were similar in shape. The 5in hooped wheels had diameters of 42in in fore and 54in in hind. The body was 126in by 47in at floor, with a depth of 12in, and may be regarded as typical.

Forsey of Symondsbury, near Bridport, built a waggon for Joseph Gibbs of Moorbath Farm, which was similar in all respects. Forsey built another without bows for the same farmer that has a body no more than 114in by 47in, and 13in deep. The 3in wheels were 40in and 50in in diameter respectively (see Figs 23 and 24).

Pearcy of Payhembury, near Cullompton; Reed of Morchard, sixteen miles north-west of Exeter on the Barnstaple road; and Langford of Northleigh, near Barnstaple, built in much the same style with Devon characteristics. In Dorset, Plenty, of Wootton, near Sherborne made simpler waggons, but with all-round excellence. One that I noted, for John Davis of North Wootton, was dated 1912 and had the smallest dimensions I have recorded. The body was 108in by 46in and ran on 3in wheels, 38in and 47in fore and hind. The shafts were hinged by splinter-bar to four hounds. The sheer-

raved body had twenty spindles on each side and the head- and tail-boards were set *between* the sides. The body was painted yellow. This waggon was the smallest of all that I recorded in the West of England.

The low-sided little waggons of Cornwall had small fore-wheels that allowed a full lock. The guards over the hind-wheels, sometimes of wood, sometimes of iron, were arched to keep the load clear of the wheels. The structure of the sides varied a little from one maker to another, but usually the angle was about 45° with about twelve spindles backed by panel boards. The separate fore- and hind-carriages were each bolted and braced to the floor members and a set of turntable rings was nearly always fitted. There were medium-size ladders steeply set to fore and aft with a rope roller on the hind ladder. The wheels, with treads of 2½in or 3in, had diameters of 30in and 45in for fore and hind and usually were spoked twelve all round. Not many were noted, but examples were seen at Trevose Head, at Cartuther, near Liskeard, and between Fowey and Par. David Wray found the best example near Polperro,

32 **Cornwall:** Built at Polperro c1910. Body blue, undercarriage red. (*From a diagram drawn by David Wray*)

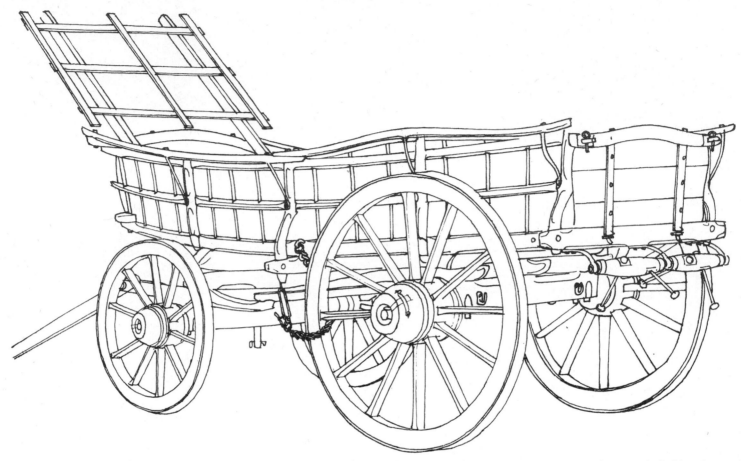

33 **Cornwall:** Chest-waggon built at Lifton, near Launceston, in 1894. Body blue, undercarriage red

from which he prepared a diagram. The spindles on this waggon were finely turned and the whole waggon was much better finished than most.

The chest-waggon, or 'Chester', was fairly deep, and had open raves set at a medium distance from the top and bowed very shallowly over the hind-wheels. The fore-end of the body suggested the unlikely influence of Hereford by the forward rise of the body and the arched head-rail. The usual rope roller was fitted under the hind-beam. The 3in wheels were much larger and slightly dished. Braking was by drop chain on both sides. The body had quite slender middle-raves with thirteen spindles and was painted (Devon) near Launceston (Cornwall), on the margin of the Tamar blue on a salmon undercarriage. One example was made at Lifton

valley, which region could have had its own hybrid culture. Much of it is inaccessible other than by farm tracks and footpaths.

Wiltshire, South Gloucestershire and Glamorganshire

Within the region consisting of Gloucestershire south of the city, Wiltshire and, surprisingly, the Vale of Glamorgan, one found designs of waggon with many features in common. They were dominated by waggons which had full bow-raves and a 'half-moon' nameboard on the head and were with or without head rails resembling a cow's horns. There was some evidence of a two-way, east-west exchange of ideas between the English counties, centred on the area defined by Malmesbury, Tetbury and Dursley. To the west, the Severn flows down in a wide estuary. Far away beyond the Wye, Usk and Taff lies the Vale of Glamorgan. There one may be surprised to find a waggon quite in conformity, full-bowed, half-mooned and cow-horned. Bearing in mind the lively, undying culture of the Welsh people, one may be reluctant to regard this waggon as an infiltration, yet the affinity with Gloucestershire could not be denied.

Not every waggon had bow-raves, half-moons or cow-horns. Some had bodies just deep enough to allow an easy sheer. The complication arose because either bow- or sheer-raved waggons could have a bed that was straight, crooked or waisted. And then there was the variety of colours. With all this variation, there were two features very commonly to be found; all waggons had large ladders set within the body to stand steeply, and secondly all the broad-wheel waggons had coned strakes on the front ring and a flat hoop on the back, a feature commonly found north of Gloucester. A waggon, recorded in 1950, near Stow-on-the-Wold, still carried the original branding 'James Bishop, Nympsfield, Gloucestershire' on the half-moon. The front end swept up in the Wiltshire manner, with full bows over the hind-wheels. The body had a crooked bed but no mid-raves. The out-raves were closed and the twelve robust spars had a marked rake to fore and aft, suggesting an origin in the Nailsworth district. The body sides were supported by iron Y-standards and there were four summers instead of the usual two. The shafts were hinged by draught-pin

to two hounds and the waggon ran on 8in hooped wheels. The body was yellow with a blue half-moon, carrying yellow lettering shaded red. The undercarriage was red.

Rogers of Warmley, six miles from Bristol, built a waggon for Horace Taylor of Netherells Farm, Frampton. I found this behind a pub in Winchcombe. It had the characteristic forward rise to the raves which were full-bowed. The head-board was plain and the body had a straight bed. The 4½in wheels had *two* rings of strakes and cast-iron hubs hung on iron 'through' axles supported by wooden beds. The entire waggon was painted a deep salmon.

In 1968 a waggon was noted at Great Wolford, north east of Moreton-in-Marsh. It had lately been branded 'Chandlers Farms, Brailes' (near Banbury). Close examination of the cast-iron hubs showed the maker, J. Workman, Wotton-under-Edge. The body

57

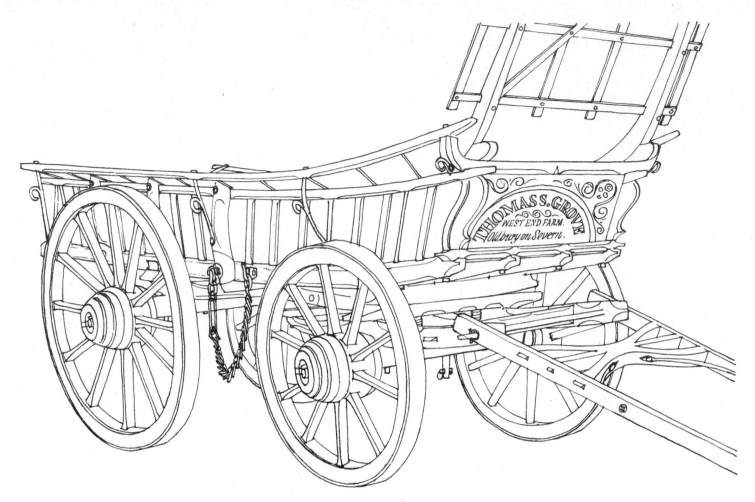

35 South Gloucestershire: Built at Oldbury-on-Severn. Body blue, undercarriage red. Note cow-horn head and half-moon panel, also 4in wheels

had a straight bed with sides that swept well up to fore, in the Wiltshire way, and the raves were fully-bowed. There were twelve flat spars on each side with the typical rake to fore and aft. The tail-board closed in the vertical position and again was unmistakably Wiltshire in its symmetrical curves with two spars arranged as an inverted V. The closed out-raves were supported midway by curved Y-standards held in iron sockets to a flush-ended main-beam. The hind standard was the usual straight Y-iron standing on a projecting beam. There were two wooden staves above the hind-axle held by iron sockets, which were similar in shape to those on the Nympsfield waggon. The half-moon was present, but the head-rave had the deep concave of Wiltshire. The detachable body was held in place by two angle-irons on the hind bolster. The

body, painted blue, ran on 3in hooped wheels, hung on unsupported iron 'through' axles. The undercarriage was red.

A waggon noted in 1952 was made at Oldbury for Thomas Grove of West End Farm, Oldbury. It had the straight-bed body without mid-raves and a fair sheer that left the out-raves just clear of the hind-wheels. There were twelve half-round wood spars set with the typical rake that gave the waggon a racy look. Like many waggons in the region, the main standard, of wood, was clamped to a flush-ended main-beam, but once again the hind standard was the iron Y. Also, there were two chamfered staves above the hind-axle. Pig-tail rope hooks were forged to each of the iron rave stays supporting closed raves. At the head was the expected cow-horn and half-moon. The shafts were draught-pinned to two hounds and the waggon ran on 4in hooped wheels. The spoking was ten in fore and twelve in hind. Both the body and the ladders were blue. The half-moon was edged with red and the white lettering and whirligigs

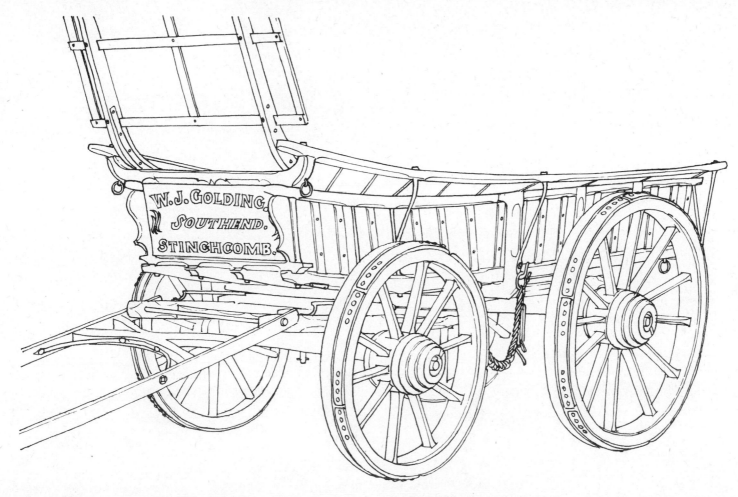

in each corner were in white, shaded red. The undercarriage was deep salmon.

To the south of Brooksthorpe, between Stroud and Gloucester, a waggon was noted in 1949. By sale, it had moved from Stinchcombe, near Dursley, where it had belonged to W. J. Golding of Southend Farm, Stinchcombe. It was not dissimilar to the Oldbury waggon but lacked the half-moon and had broad wheels shod with strakes and hoops in the Gloucester way. Braking appeared to be by drop chain alone, with chafing cleats on the hind-wheel spokes. The blue body had a deep salmon head-board with white lettering shaded black. The undercarriage was salmon. This waggon also had 'Wiltshire' ladders.

The Welsh Folk Museum has three examples of waggons from the Vale of Glamorgan, two fully bowed and one with sheer-raves. The late example came from Pyle, branded 'Griffith Thomas'. One bow-rave was branded 'Phillip Phillips, Llanishen Fach', and

36 **South Gloucestershire:** Builder not known. Stinchcombe is between Dursley and Berkeley. Body blue, head-panel and undercarriage red. Note strakes and hoops together on broad wheels

the other 'Thomas Morgan, Sker' (near Porthcawl). All had narrow wheels, two had van-type naves, but otherwise they were 'en famille' with the Gloucesters. Another bow-waggon (see Fig 3) was recovered at North Petherton, near Bridgwater. It was branded 'Alner Bowring'. None of these waggons were lacking in the matter of finish and all were well and strongly made and looked very handsome. All had shafts more elaborately constructed than their English cousins and the head-rails especially called for attention. I have no records of any waggons made by James of Llantrisant, who had a reputation for exacting work in the making of gambos. Reference has been made to the influence of Wiltshire and in the western part of that county one encountered the influence of south Gloucester and in the county as a whole all the impress

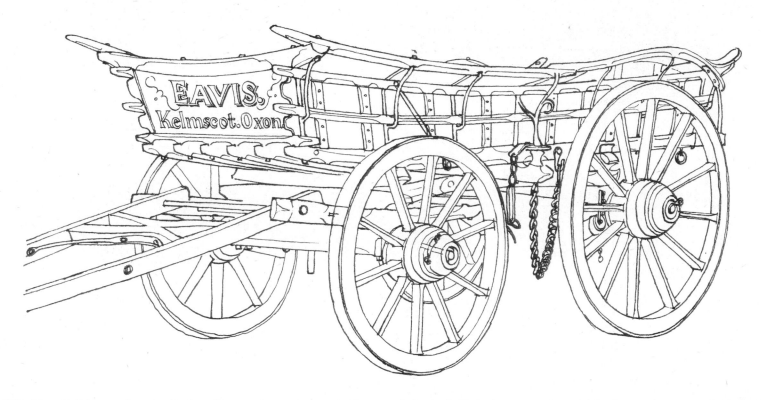

37 **Wiltshire:** Builder not known. Body yellow, undercarriage red. Note the shafts set between the hounds

of the neighbouring counties which, in turn, accepted ideas from the 'island' county. For purposes of clarity the Wiltshire designs have been termed A, B and C. Certain features of design have already been noted. In Wiltshire every known example had a straight bed.

Design A might be regarded as the parent and was to be seen in considerable numbers in every part of the county, and often beyond into the neighbouring counties. It had full bows and closed raves rising quite steeply forward, with the out-raves extended. The iron standards at the main- and hind-beams were all straight Y-pattern and all transverse beams projected normally. Each side had ten to fourteen flat spars, rather less raked than in Gloucestershire, but the two wood staves above the hind-axle were nearly always present. Middle-raves were absent. Most waggons had plain head-panels but a few had two or more spars. The tail-boards were unmistakable with symmetrical top-edge and inverted V-spars. All head-rails were deeply concave. The wheel treads varied; most were 6in, double straked, but a few had 3in wheels, all spoked ten

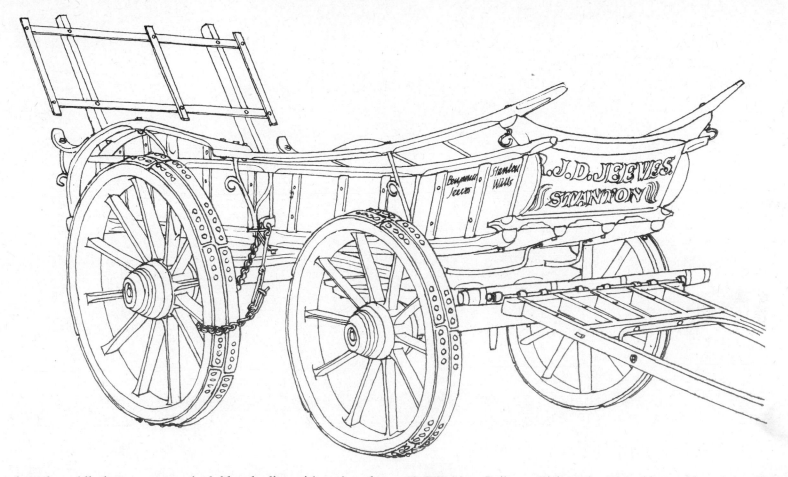

and twelve. All these waggons had blue bodies with red under-carriages.

Design B had similar overall lines, but had heavily panelled sides *and* tail-board, both with mid-rave. With both head and tail set athwart the sides, this design hinted at strong influence from Dorset, although both examples recorded were noted far away, one at Kelmscott, near Lechlade, and the other at Ogbourne St Andrew, near Marlborough. Some had their shafts hinged by splinter-bars and had twin sliders on the hounds. Wheel treads varied from 3½in to 6in. The waggon from Kelmscott belonged to Eavis and was painted yellow, while the second was branded William Wadman, Ogbourne St Andrew. For a long time it stood outside a farm at Sydmondham between Kingsclere and Newbury.

Design C appears to have centred on Devizes and barely nodded to its neighbours. Two examples were noted, one at Ashbury had a sheer profile and a cow-horn head-rail, but the second belonging to Henry Goodall & Son, Park Farm, Worton (near Devizes), had mid-raves and a body deep enough to dispense with bows. Each

38 **Wiltshire:** Built at Highworth. Body blue, with red head-panel; undercarriage red. Note that main-beam is absent

39 Wiltshire: Built in the Wylye Valley. Body blue, with red head-panel; undercarriage red. Note unusual hingeing of double shafts. (*From photographs by Edward Jewell*)

side had twelve flat spars, slightly raked, and there were four summers and splinter-bars. Lock was restricted by chains each side suspended from sides to the hounds. The blue body ran on 3in wheels shod with hoops.

A fine example of design A used to stand in the yard of a wheelwright at Highworth, north of Swindon (now occupied by an office block in glass and steel). The red head-board was branded 'R. J. D. Jeeves, Stanton, Wiltshire', while a black plate on the fore off side read 'Benjamin Jeeves, North Farm, Stanton, Wilts' (father and son). The lettering was in yellow, shaded black on a red panel. The blue body was fully bowed with closed raves. The

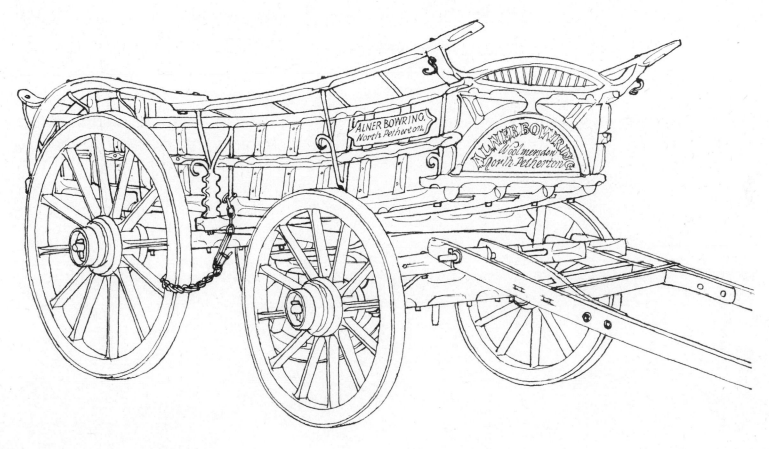

shafts were hinged by splinter-bar and the broad wheels were deeply dished with two rings of strakes.

I am indebted to Edward Jewell for photographs of an unusual variant of this design which he recorded at Corton, in the Wylye Valley between Wilton and Warminster. It was branded 'Jonas Rugg, Manor Farm, Cortington' (old spelling). It had double shafts which were draught-pinned at the hounds. The construction was so ingenious as to defy verbal description (Fig 39). The owner has an interesting collection from various parts of Wessex. A curious feature of the waggons at Corton, Kelmscott and Ogbourne St Andrew was that the wooden part of the bow stopped a foot short of the hind-beam and terminated with an iron rod.

40 **Glamorganshire:** Builder not known. Body blue, undercarriage salmon. North Petherton is south of Bridgwater

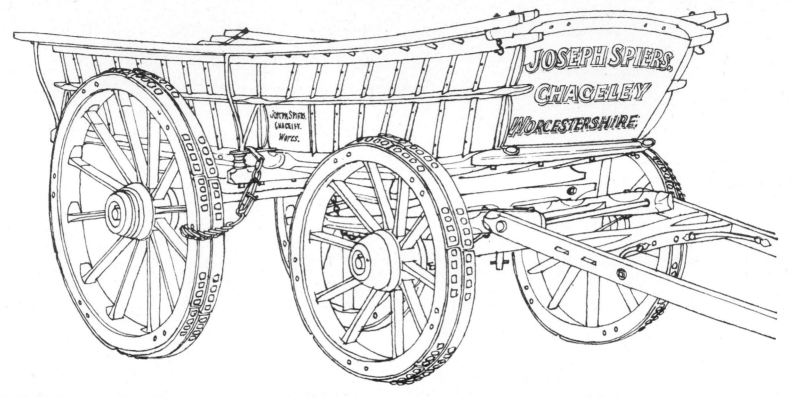

JOSEPH SPIERS. CHACELEY WORCESTERSHIRE.

41 North Gloucestershire: Built by Gascoigne of Forthampton, Tewkesbury, in 1850. Body originally yellow, later repainted blue, now restored to yellow. Undercarriage red

North Gloucestershire, Worcestershire

The Gloucestershire plain, north of the city, is bounded on the east by the Cotswold escarpment and on the west by the Malverns, which ridge peters out southward toward the Forest of Dean and continues in a more determined way northward to Wyre Forest. Beyond this there lies the vast conurbation of the midlands. The traveller bound for the west, on reaching the escarpment, becomes aware that he or she is leaving behind the stone-walled uplands and entering a land of orchards, close fields and dairy cattle. The county town of Gloucester was similar to Banbury in that it was a meeting place of various designs of waggon.

The designs of the counties of Gloucester and Worcester together formed a loose association that penetrated westward to the Forest of Dean and northward to Bromsgrove. The region was isolated topographically from any influences from the Marches, the Cotswolds and the country south of Gloucester. Within this association, the diversity of designs was such as to make identity difficult and to suggest a marked individuality among the wheelwrights. There was no one design that could be taken as typical of the region. A waggon made by Healey & Son of Gloucester may be considered first. It had a crooked bed, but the normal front piece of wood forming the base of the head-board was replaced by a flat iron bar.

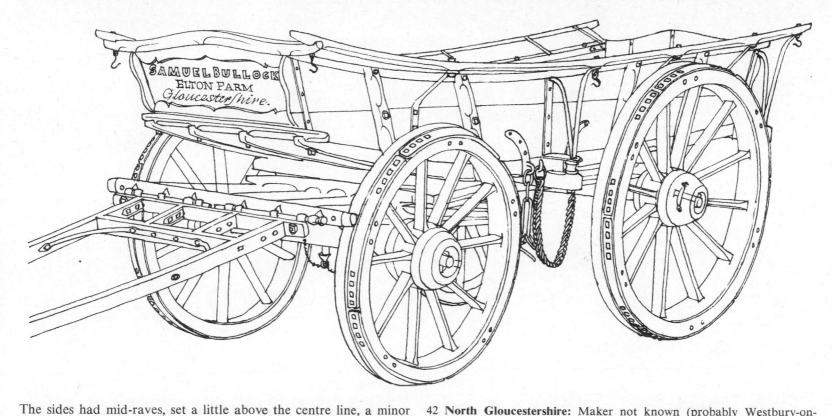

The sides had mid-raves, set a little above the centre line, a minor point to be noted among many of the waggons. Of the sixteen spindles, three were of iron, and the sides were supported by plain round iron N-standards at main- and hind-beams. Behind the fore pillow there was a wooden cupid's bow with an iron stay to support the out-raves, and there were two more cupid's bows above the hind bolster. The open out-raves carried six rope hooks. The tail-board, like the head-board, was plain and barrel-hinged, with the hinge bars curved over at the top, ending in forged rings to fit the ends of the raves. The shafts were draught-pinned to four hounds which were cyma curved. The 4in wheels had van-type naves with ten spokes in fore and twelve in hind. The waggon was fully braked. The body was blue with a red head panel so far faded that the branding was indecipherable. This waggon was noted near High-leadon between Gloucester and Newent (see Fig 43).

C. P. Teague had a reputation as maker, well upheld by a waggon made for W. R. Fowler of Tirley. This waggon had a sheer profile with double-raves and high-set mid-raves, below which the fore-end of the body turned in quite sharply, to improve the lock. The front beam was replaced by a flat iron bar. There was a decided fore and aft rake to the sixteen spindles and the body sides were supported by curved N-standards of iron, with additional cupid's bows. There

42 **North Gloucestershire:** Maker not known (probably Westbury-on-Severn). Body ochre, with blue ground within white cartouche. Undercarriage red

43 **Gloucester:** Built by Healey & Son, Westcott Street. Body blue with red head-panel and undercarriage. Note flat iron bar instead of wooden beam. A crooked-bed waggon with a Shropshire fore-carriage

were three summers, with the main-pin right through the middle summer. The tail-board was plain, but the head had a middle-rave and the body was waist-bedded. The shafts were attached by draught-pin to four hounds. The broad wheels had the expected coned strakes on the front ring and a flat hoop on the back. They were well dished and had ten spokes in the fore-wheels and twelve in the hind-wheels. The short fore-ladder fitted flatly between the raves, but the hind-ladder was missing. Braking was by drop chain and roller. The body was painted yellow with well-drawn branding on the head and the initials 'W.R.F.' with 'T.' below on the tail. On the fore off side a long white strip carried the name and address of the owner. This strip was frequently to be noted on waggons north of Gloucester and out as far as Montgomery and Builth.

Another waggon, once in the same ownership, is now in the collection at Acton Beauchamp, near Bromyard, owned by J. G. Fowler. It is a much simpler design but has broad wheels, straked in the Gloucester way.

A waggon closely resembling the Teague is likewise in Mr Fowler's collection. It was much travelled, having been noted by the writer at Gotherington, and was branded 'Joseph Spiers, Chaceley, Worcestershire', in fine lettering on a blue body. Close examination, however, showed a yellow ground where the blue had flaked off, leaving one to guess again the original owner. It had some features of the Teague plus a waisted bed, but minus the mid-rave on the head. This waggon was a broad-wheeler built by Gascoigne, of Forthampton, near Tewkesbury (see Fig 41).

Further to make one puzzle, the Kirbee Museum at Whitchurch, near Ross, has a nearly identical waggon in first-class condition, made by Moore of Abergavenny in 1900. Since it bore no resemblance to Monmouth designs one must presume that Moore served

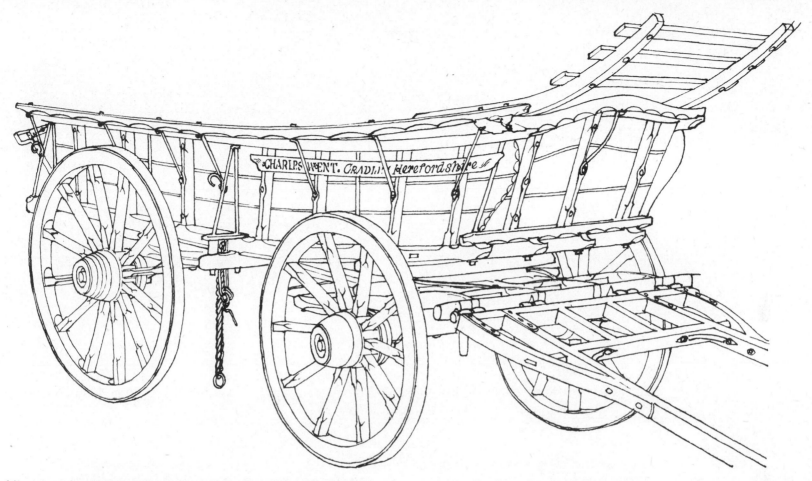

his apprenticeship in Gloucestershire before setting up as master in Abergavenny. The wheels were narrow and ran on oil-axles.

It was near Bishops Cleeve that a quite different design was recorded in 1964. The sheer-profile body was so shallow that the out-raves only just cleared the hind-wheels. The frame had a crooked bed and the sides, without mid-raves, had twelve flat spars raked fore and aft and supported by iron N-standards. There were two summers and the shafts were draught-pinned to two hounds. The broad wheels were shod with strakes on the front ring and hoops on the back. The spoking of ten on all wheels came as a surprise. I recollected a Sussex waggon I had once noted near Steyning, with fourteen spokes on all wheels, and concluded that the particular wheelwright (of Bishops Cleeve?) had tremendous confidence in his wheels. The body was blue with a red head carrying the branding 'Walter Redman, Grange Farm, Bishops Cleeve, Gloucestershire' in white, shaded black. The undercarriage was red.

44 Worcestershire: Built in 1910 by Paterson of Storridge, Herefordshire. Body ochre, with pale blue grooves and orange name-strip; undercarriage red. Note spokes and elbow-shafts

Jones of Tewkesbury made a waggon for H. Roberts of Washbourne (near Bredon Hill), Gloucestershire. The hooped wheels had 2½in treads with twelve spokes in fore and fourteen in hind. The wheels had oil-axles with the builder's name incised. The two outer hounds were quite straight, but the inner pair curved out to join the outer, to which the shafts were attached by draught-pin. There were three summers, with the main-pin right through. The body had a waisted bed and the sides had the spars set edge on and raked fore and aft, not graduated as was usual but set parallel in each group. There were no mid-raves and the sides were supported by N-standards and there were rings to take corner poles. No ladders were present. The yellow body had a red undercarriage.

45 **Monmouthshire:** Built by Bradley of Onen. Body blue, undercarriage red. Restored by the Rural Crafts Museum, Llanvapley, Abergavenny. A small waggon, with 38in and 50in wheels, suited to the hilly countryside

Another waggon now in Mr Fowler's collection which was first noted at Storridge, just in Herefordshire, appeared to be typical of those built in the vicinity of Worcester. It had a straight bed with seven flat spars set vertically aft but raked forward. The sheer profile had closed raves with distinctive chamfering on the underside, which was repeated on the Hereford-type head-rails, which were double. The elbow shafts were hinged by splinter-bar to four hounds which had cyma curves fore and aft of the crossing. The 2¼in wheels were spoked ten and twelve and with diameters of 45in and 55in were a little smaller than most in the region. The buff, or ochre, body had two horizontal grooves painted pale blue and the name-strip on the fore off side was in orange with the branding 'L. Moseley, Storridge' in black. This waggon built by Patterson, of Storridge, Herefordshire, had been made originally for Charles Went of Cradley.

A quite different waggon was located near Westbury-on-Severn, where the riverside meadows meet the heavily wooded Forest of Dean. It was branded 'Samuel Bullock, Elton Farm, Gloucestershire'. It had a straight bed and an easy sheer to a body so shallow that the out-raves only just cleared the hind-wheels. Support was given by V-standards of iron and four robust wooden staves, held by iron clasps and well-chamfered. The closed, wide-set out-raves carried rope hooks (see Fig 42). The frame had two summers and the otherwise plain head-panel was enclosed by a 'cartouche' of wood. The plain tail-board had barrel hinges, the straps of which terminated in forged rings to fit the rave ends. The shafts were hinged by splinter-bar to four hounds and the waggon ran on 6in wheels which were doubly straked and deeply dished, with ten spokes in the the fore-wheels and twelve in the hind-wheels. The body, painted ochre, had a blue panel within the cartouche and the branding was white, shaded red. The undercarriage likewise was red.

About the turn of the century there were at least two wheelwrights in Bromsgrove – Daniel Giles and John Martin – producing

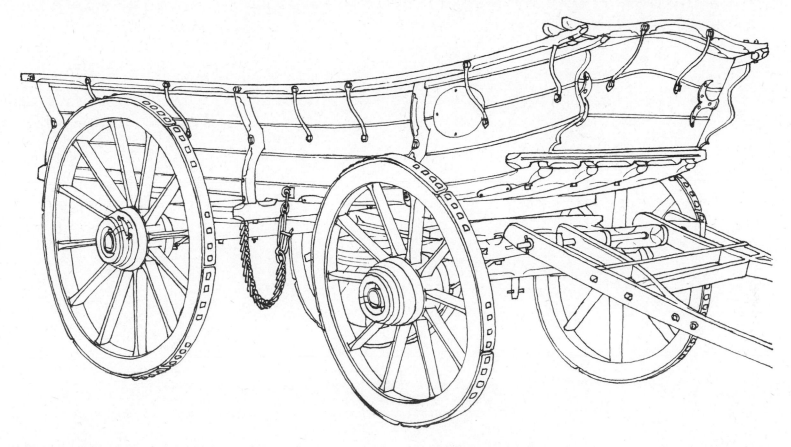

vehicles so similar that one surmised that the one had been apprenticed to the other. I found a Giles at Much Marcle, in Herefordshire, branded 'F. B. Matthews, Brampton', and a second branded 'F. W. Dale, The Thorne, Birley, Herefordshire', and in the Kirbee collection, already mentioned, there is an almost identical example, unbranded but carrying the maker's plate (Giles). These waggons were really of the barge type since they were fully-locking. That in the Kirbee collection had broad wheels and oil-axles, a remarkable combination that made one careful of rating any waggon anywhere by its features. The Kirbee waggon was equipped with half-thripples which were really very large ladders. It also had a large rectangular frame called a cratch for carrying livestock. The first two waggons had 3½in wheels with diameters of 35in and 53 in. All three had ochre bodies with three grooves, painted white or blue. The Dale waggon, now restored, is on show, with a late Devon, by Hensley of Exmouth, in the gardens belonging to Frank H. Dale Ltd., of Leominster.

46 Herefordshire: Built at or near Presteigne. Body blue with red grooves, undercarriage red. Built to carry thripples and boards. Note large, narrow wheels

The Marches
The region of the Marches contains many hills that are bold enough to sub-divide it into smaller regions, through which fast rivers flow ultimately to join the Severn estuary. The region is mainly grazing country, with sheep everywhere in the north and west, and beef cattle and sheep in the south-east. Taken overall, cereals are less important, but in the south-east cereals, hops and fruit are dominant crops.

Bearing in mind the comparatively small waggons in the West of England, one might expect to find small waggons in the Marches, but this was not the case. Without exception, they were large and strongly built. Every one had a straight bed and sheer profile and the division in design was in the type of framework fitted to increase the capacity, in the shape of the wooden standards and the arrangement of the out-raves. There were two 'parent' designs. The Here-

47 **Herefordshire:** Built at Kyre c1845. Body blue, undercarriage red. Shown with charcoal boards fitted. Note 4½in coned hoops

ford, which had elbow standards, close-set out-raves and large harvest frames called thripples, and the Shropshire, which had 'wishbone' standards, wide-set closed raves and sills projecting over the head, all closed, and the normal ladders. The first design had variants in the counties of Hereford and Brecon, while the second had variants in Shropshire and Montgomery. In Radnorshire there were designs influenced by either 'parent' or hybrids of both. These waggons can not be 'dated' by the presence or absence of panelling, although the later Herefords *mostly* had planked bodies. Irrespective of this, almost every waggon had two or three equidistant grooves, coloured in contrast to the body colour, according to sub-regional practice. Broad wheels remained a feature, although Radnorshire waggons were nearly all built with narrow wheels.

A great many waggons in Shropshire and Herefordshire had shafts reinforced with external 'elbows', hinged by splinter-bar to four hounds, the outer pair of which were widely splayed to meet the splinter, but almost joining the inner pair at the tail, often carrying twin slider-bars. Seen in side-elevation, the hounds had cyma curves to fore and aft of the axle-bed. Although it was normal practice to gear three horses singly for a full load, it was not unknown, in the Forest of Clun, for as many as eight horses to be geared in four pairs. Readers who are familiar with the roads will understand why.

Every waggon had ten spokes in the fore-wheels and twelve in the hind. The vehicles could not be 'zoned' according to colour, although the Shropshires, east of Craven Arms, were blue while those to the west were yellow, together with those in Montgomery.

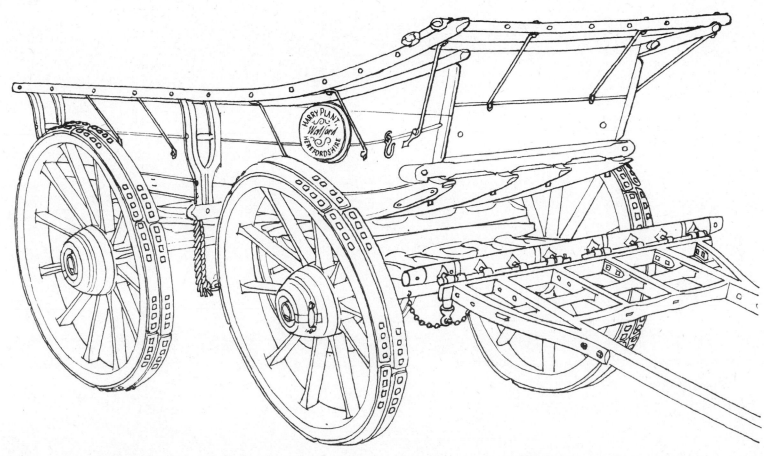

Elsewhere, in Herefordshire, Radnorshire and Monmouthshire they could be any colour, blue, ochre or yellow. Even the blue might be Prussian, Saxe or indigo. Generally, the undercarriages varied from scarlet in the east to salmon-orange in the west.

In the north-west, where gambos, wheelcars and even sleds were used, it is perhaps surprising that waggons were employed. When I first became acquainted in 1932, one could usually find a waggon or two standing outside The Anchor at the summit of the old drovers' road from Newtown. Francis of Newcastle-on-Clun, Cadwallader of Bishops Castle and Jones of Montgomery, made large waggons which were to be compared favourably with the best in the country. They were all panel-bodied with wishbones or elbows, projecting sills and large, well-dished wheels, some broad, some narrow, all with yellow bodies. The fore-carriages were as described above, with the main-pin inverted. These waggons were

48 **Herefordshire:** Built at Brampton Bryan. Body yellow, with one white groove; undercarriage red. Built to carry ladders. Note the Clun influence in all features

never branded on the panelled heads but Cadwallader's had a long, white name-strip on the fore off side, while Francis's had the small lettering on the near-side dirt-board over the hind-axle—hardly the best place.

Waggons built by Jones of Montgomery derived from Bishops Castle but were rather simpler and mostly ran on narrow wheels. The tail-board was in the form of a cratch, with open spindles. A good example from Criggion is owned by J. G. Fowler of Acton Beauchamp, who also possesses a Radnorshire waggon from Llanbadarn Fynydd, in the Ithon valley. This is one of those hybrids with both wishbone and elbow standards and looks very gay with a yellow body and orange wheels.

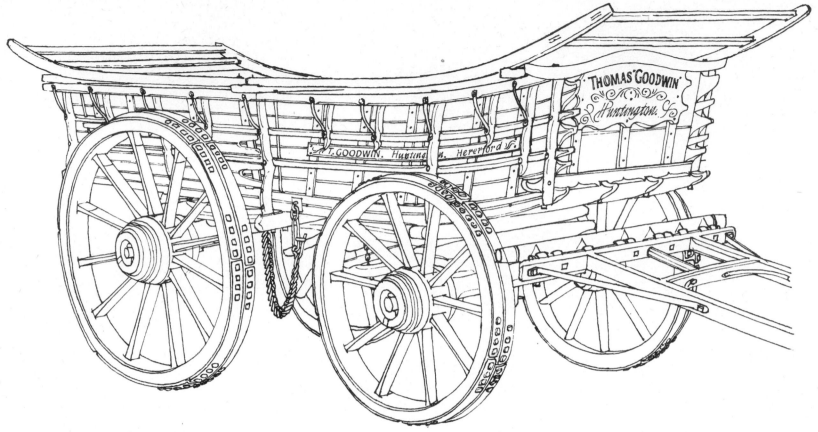

49 Herefordshire: Built at Kington. Body blue, with red grooves; under-carriage red. Name-board and name-strip white

The river Onny that flows down from near the Stiperstones is the boundary between the Shropshires west and east. From there, eastward to the Severn the waggons were much simpler, with blue plank bodies, nearly all on narrow wheels. There were, of course, not a few with yellow bodies. The Shropshires and the Herefords were similar in respect of their undercarriages, but the Herefords were more diverse in design and may be grouped as follows:

1 Central and east to the Malverns
2 North-east, between Bromyard and Tenbury
3 North, about Leintwardine
4 West, between Kington and Hay
5 North-east of Leominster
6 Ross

Groups 1, 2 and 4 were the most characteristic and the most

numerous. The Bromyard and Kington waggons were panelled and painted blue, but many, especially from the centre, had plank bodies, variously coloured. All of them had elbow standards and close-set out-raves, and most ran on broad wheels. One waggon, preserved at Tundridge Farm, Suckley, has broad wheels shod with 6in strakes which join diagonally, with flush nails in groups of four. Mr Griffiths, who farms at Munsley, has a plank-bodied waggon on broad wheels that is a little smaller than most.

The Bromyard waggons were quite large and were elaborately panelled and with close out-raves unusually supported by ten spindles each side from the mid-raves. The twelve flat spars had their feet projecting below the side frames. Mr Nott, who farmed Brockmanton Court until a few years ago, had a fine example, built near Kyre not later than 1850, in first-rate condition. The name-board on the head was lettered by a Leominster man in 1905. A similar waggon, in advanced decay, was noted near Eardisland. The 6½in wheels were shod with 3¼in and 2¾in strakes, with diameters of 48in and 58in. The main elbow had a back slope. The waggons in these groups were all equipped with both thripples

72

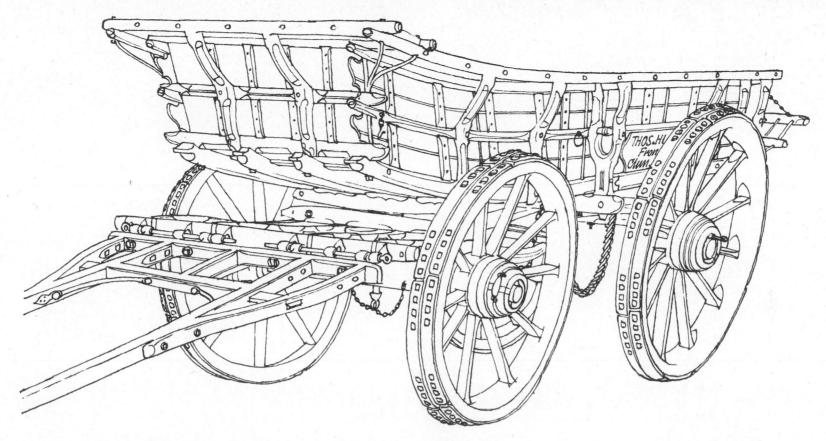

50 **Clun:** Built at Newcastle-on-Clun by Francis, c1905. Body yellow, with blue grooves; undercarriage salmon. Note the curious position of branding on dirtboards

and charcoal boards. Twice a year the hop growers sent convoys of waggons to collect charcoal for hop drying, from either the Wyre Forest or the Forest of Dean, and the boards were fitted to deepen the bodies. We shall find all through this book that in the past the farmer collected his fuel and conveyed his crops to the buyer, but that today all fuel is brought by the merchant and all crops are collected by the buyer.

Waggons made at Leintwardine and Brampton Bryan were influenced by Clun in most features, though many had plank bodies, carrying a fore-ladder over the sill. A good example was made for Harry Plant of Walford by Bowen of Brampton Bryan. It had a yellow body with the owner's name well lettered on a black disc on the off-side. The undercarriage had four hounds splinter-barred to elbowed shafts and the broad wheels were hung on wooden arms.

In group 4, between Kington and Hay, Beddoes of Brilley made beautiful waggons, fully panelled and painted a deep sea-green blue. With mid-raves and close-set out-raves carrying panelled charcoal boards, they appeared at first glance to have two mid-

raves on each side. Beddoes's waggons had double shafts and narrow wheels. The name-board on the head was white and of ornamental shape, varying from one waggon to the next. There is a fine example still at Upper Mowley, near Titley, once owned by James Davies and dated 1900. The Welsh Folk Museum has one, branded 'Samuel Meredith, Fuallt, 1897', and there is a third at Michaelchurch-on-Arrow, owned by S. K. Williams of Glyn Afon. I have records of a similar waggon built at Kington for Thomas Goodwin of Huntington. This one *did* have double mid-raves and carried a set of thripples. The body colour was similar and likewise the name-board. All these waggons had a long white name-strip on the fore off side. Here and there one came across the 'non-conformist' of which two were notable. A waggon was noted at Marston, near Lyonshall, built at Leysters for S. H. Thomas of Woonton Court and now in safe hands. It had a plank body, wide-set closed raves, supported by tri-branching iron standards (also

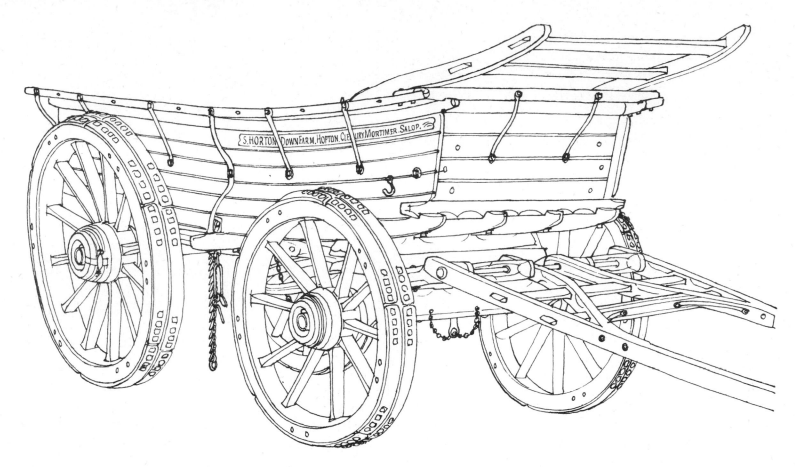

51 **Shropshire** (Corvedale): Built at Cleobury Mortimer. Body blue, with four red grooves; undercarriage red

noted on another at Fromes Hill). The undercarriage was, like all Herefords, superbly chamfered with the body resting freely but stabilised by a wood block known as a monkey. Some Herefords had a slotted bolster to fit the frames. This waggon was blue with a scarlet undercarriage and carried ladders but no boards.

Another, from Nash, near Presteigne, is now owned by Mr & Mrs Sparrow of Eardisland. The blue planked body had back sloping elbows, close-set out-raves and twin head-rails. The shafts were draught-pinned to four hounds and the body at floor measured 135½ x 43½ x 17in (deep) against the normal 142 x 48 x 21. The wheelbase and track were 72 x 60 (over) against 81 x 66 (over). The Nash also ran on 2½in wheels. As with all these plank-bodied waggons, the planks (1¾in thick) were held by thin through-bolts. Panel boards were usually about ⅝in. According to Mr Kirby of Whitchurch, ladders were called half-thripples in Herefordshire.

Ross was a district so 'non-conformist' that the association was not immediately apparent. A good example was made for L. B. Lee of How Caple Court by Turner of Ross, not before 1900. It had a shallow body with closed wide-set raves. It was panel-lined in white on a blue body with excellent lettering on the head. The fore-carriage had turntable rings.

Breconshire waggons built in the Talgarth district strongly echoed Hereford practice in every feature except for the absence of out-raves, which made the body appear much narrower. C. M. Morris of Pistil Farm, Llanfihangel-tal-y-llyn, owned one. It was blue with salmon wheels, broad and double-straked. It carried thripples but no boards and carried the branding on an ornamental white board similar to Brilley and Kington. In 1948 I noted my first Brecon at Inglesham, near Lechlade, almost identical but not quite.

Pen-y-bont might be considered the hub of Radnorshire, where meet five roads from Knighton, Leominster, Builth, Rhayader and Newtown, and the waggons made in the valleys showed

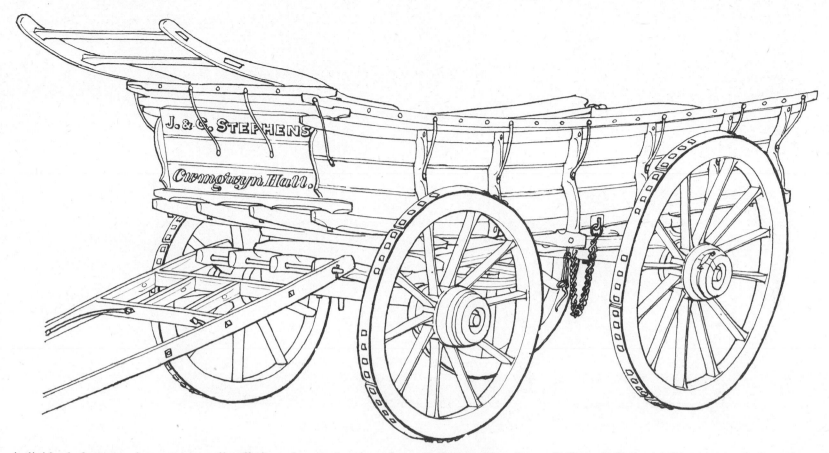

individual features but an overall affinity. Aaron Lewis, who worked at Rhos grûg (Llanbister Road Station), made plank-sided waggons finished in blue, with elbows and cupid's bows to the sides. The close-set raves carried thripples and boards and the undercarriage conformed to Hereford, but ran on narrow wheels. One such waggon, made for J. T. Stokes of Cwm-y-caist, near Rhos grûg, is now owned by the potter, D. B. Weakes, at Pen-y-bont.

In the upper Teme valley, near Beguildy, a waggon was noted at Cwmgwyn Hall, farmed by J. and C. Stephens, and was probably made at Melin-y-grogue, downstream toward Knighton. It had elbows, closed raves, front sill and ladders. The shafts were draught-pinned to four cyma-curved hounds, and the 3in wheels were shallowly dished. The colours were buff and red. A further example was noted at Knighton on Llanshay Farm. In all details it closely resembled the previous waggon and was branded•'James Preece, Llanshay, Knighton, Radnorshire' on a long white strip.

In Monmouthshire, Bradley was building at Onen (Llanfihangel-ystern-Llwern) which lies off the Abergavenny—Monmouth road.

52 **Radnorshire** (Teme Valley): Built at Melin-y-grogue. Body ochre, undercarriage red.

John Thompson has prepared diagrams of a Bradley made for Evan Jones, Cefn, Llanarth (see Fig 45). This had a panelled body with spars raked fore and aft. The 4in wheels were small at 38in and 50in and the waggon was clearly designed for the exceptionally hilly country. At Wolves Newton, near Usk, there were three generations of Lewises at work and at Llangattwg, Jones & Sons were making a modified design of boat-waggon (surely the most westerly of this type).

The majority of waggons in the region appear to have been equipped solely with the drop chain for braking, although several makers, including Beddoes, fitted all three brakes. The drop chain was made from two lengths, the shorter ending in the sliding dog-hook being of straight links, while the longer, wrapping length was made usually of single twist chain and very often of double twist chain. Occasionally a straight-link chain was fitted. The

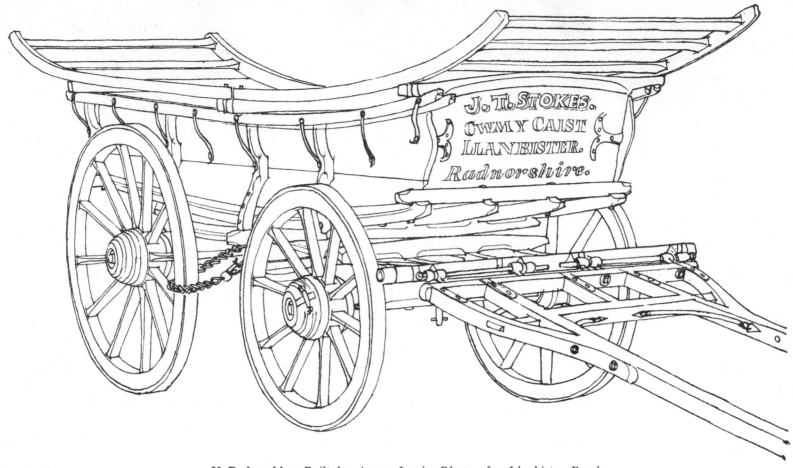

53 **Radnorshire:** Built by Aaron Lewis, Rhos grûg, Llanbister Road Station. Body blue, with salmon thripples; undercarriage salmon. Note the influence from Herefordshire

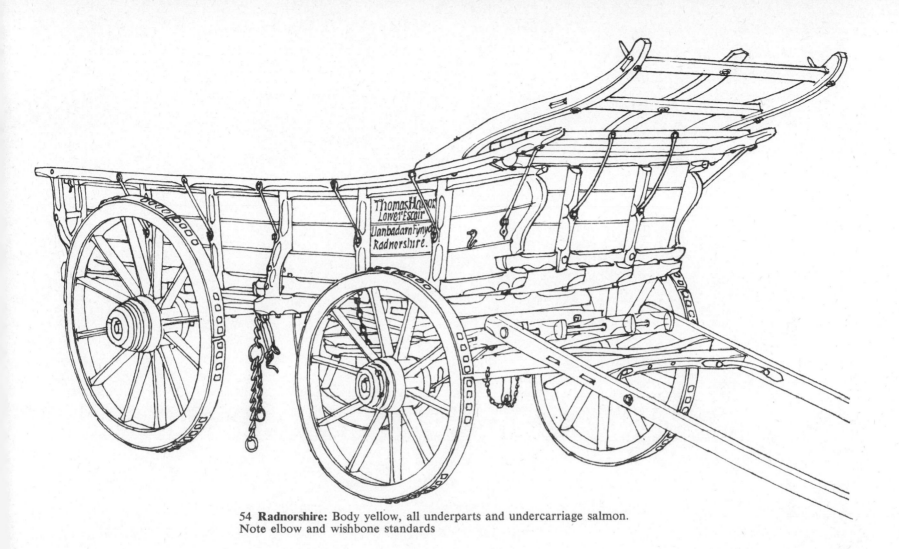

54 Radnorshire: Body yellow, all underparts and undercarriage salmon.
Note elbow and wishbone standards

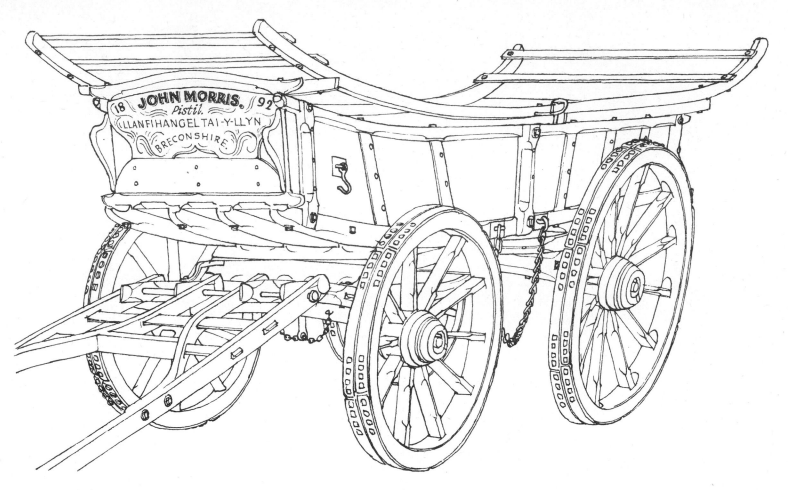

55 Breconshire: Built at Talgarth in 1892. Body blue, with white name-board; undercarriage salmon. Note absence of out-raves

purpose of the twist was to minimise chafing of spokes and felloes. The angle between the spokes and felloes on the bearing sides was faced with an angled cleat, so that the wheelwright knew an off wheel from a near when removed from the waggon. The presence of elaborate chamfering on the undercarriage of an otherwise austere plank-bodied waggon may seem odd, but the explanation may be that the change from the earlier ornately panel-bodied design did not affect the undercarriage.

There were several types of lock-chain, the most common being from the main-beam to the fore-bolster, but a most interesting one was that which ran from hind axle-bed to fore-bolster with chain suspension at three intermediate points to reduce sway.

It is not possible to make a hard and fast statement about body colours, or the number of grooves and their colours, but the following may be treated as a guide:

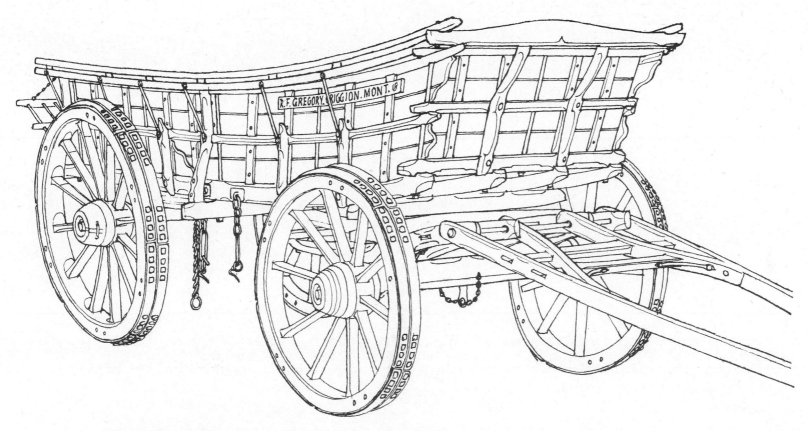

R.F.GREGORY. BUGGION. MONT. &

HEREFORD: Blue bodies with two white grooves on plank, or one red groove above and one below the middle-rave, or two red grooves on plank
Buff bodies with two blue grooves or three red grooves

SHROPSHIRE: Blue bodies with three red grooves
Buff bodies with one to three white grooves
Yellow bodies with two or three blue grooves

RADNOR: Buff bodies with two red or two blue grooves
Blue bodies without grooves

56 **Montgomery:** Built at Llanymynech. Body yellow, undercarriage salmon

I would attribute colours and grooves more to the inclination of individual makers rather than to any regional practice, but the matter seems inconclusive.

The counties of Derby, Stafford and Denbigh
Because we tend to associate Derbyshire with the Peak and because Staffordshire is synonymous with the Black Country and the potter-

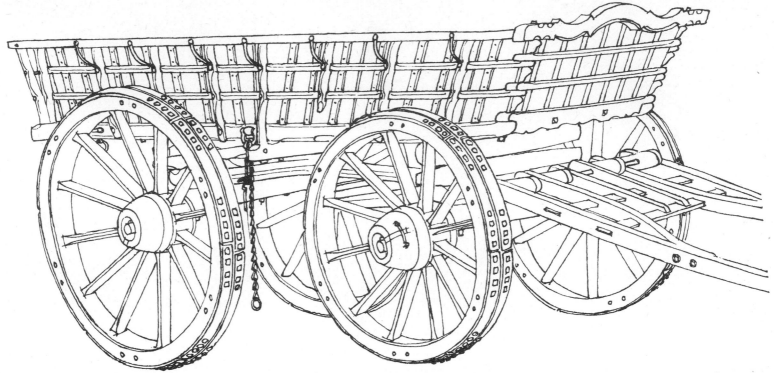

57 **Denbighshire:** Body blue or red; undercarriage red

ies, we may overlook those parts which are neither Peak nor Black.

The later nineteenth-century industries had their origins in small workshops and cottages. We remember that these industries derived their power from water and that a good head of water was to be found in the valleys. So it was that these industries were situated cheek-by-jowl with types of agriculture and sheep farming which had been practised from very early times. Because such farming had little use for the larger waggons of the corn-lands, it is the more refreshing to find that there were waggons that in their design were hardly inferior to those found elsewhere.

Mackworth, near Derby, stands close to the head of the Trent and may look eastward to Nottingham and southward to Lichfield, which in turn may look south-east to Leicester and Banbury and westward to the dairy-land of north Shropshire.

With the Vale of Clwyd in virtual isolation from the Dee, the waggons of Denbighshire were inevitably different from those in the wider lands of Shropshire. The Clwyd is largely dairy-country in which the few waggons used were only distantly associated.

I am indebted to David Wray for information about the waggons built in Derbyshire, and in particular a waggon built by Bond of Mackworth (see Fig 59). It was an interesting example for the features which distinguish it. In side elevation, the body was quite straight in all its members and had a uniform depth of 24in, emphasised by the presence of two mid-raves and the absence of out-raves. The frame had a crooked bed and was virtually unique in having straight through-members measuring 47in over at the fore- and hind-ends and 34½in midway. The junction midway was secured with two large carriage bolts and the whole structure was simple and ingenious with none of the disadvantages inherent in a waist-bed body. The side panel boards were closer together midway than at the ends and were 3in wider at the top than at the bottom. They were supported at the main- and hind-beams by iron standards. In the fore half there were six wood spindles and three iron ones nearest the main standard. In the hind half there were nine wood spindles and all fifteen wooden spindles were $\frac{7}{8}$in in diameter. The iron ones were thinner, two ½in and one $\frac{5}{8}$in. The panel boards were thinner than was usual, being $\frac{5}{8}$in instead of $\frac{3}{4}$in. The fore-spindles had a graduated rake from vertical to 14° at which angle the head-board was set, making the body 9in longer at the top-rave. The head-board was set athwart the sides, secured with $\frac{3}{4}$in iron rods through all transverses and in front of the board.

The absence of out-raves has been noted. Between the side members there were two summers and equidistantly placed on the

80

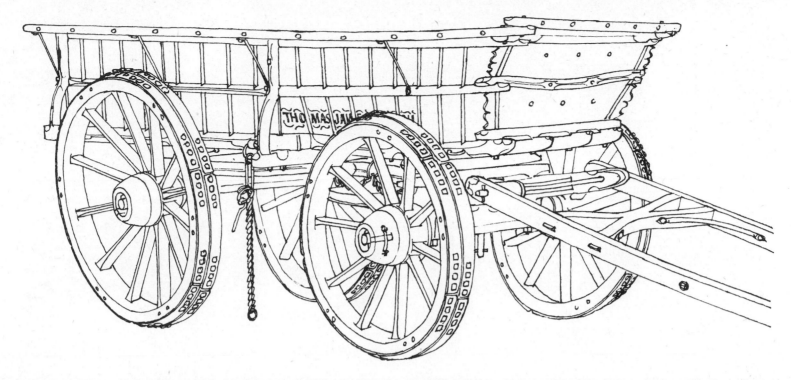

head, between the rods, were two flat iron bars to which the panel boards were bolted. At three places on the lower of the mid-raves swivelling rope-hooks were fitted. To ensure that 'bellying' did not occur under load stress, a tie-chain was attached to the top-raves, with ends secured by 'ring and dog'. There was no evidence of a tail-board, but other waggons recorded had eye bolts for hinge pins.

The tongue-pole spreaders (or braces) were not straight but had cyma curves. The two fore-carriage hounds were quite straight, but the single slider-bar was curved. The shafts had flattish elbows on the inside and were draught-pinned. The body was attached to the undercarriage by a single bolt, secured by a key below the bed. The waggon ran on 4½in wheels, shod with hoops, and had diameters of 48in in fore and 62in in hind on a track of 68in over and with a wheelbase of 73in. The wheels were spoked ten and twelve and hung on wooden axle-trees. They were flatly dished. The maximum load at harvest was accommodated by a four-part frame, with two parts overlapping the body flatly and two end frames, called gormers, standing at each end, secured by iron stays. The whole frame was 172in long by 78in wide and 44in high. The lock was restricted by straight-link chains. Two short chains joined the hind bolster to the sides, additional to the centre bolt.

The body was blue and the undercarriage apparently red, but

58 **Staffordshire:** Built at Lichfield c1860. Body yellow, undercarriage red. Fitted to carry corner poles

Wray considers that the original colour was white. There was no branding on the head, but there was a long name-strip below the top-rave at the fore-end of the off-side. Another waggon had a splinter-bar to take double shafts.

A waggon built at Lichfield, some twenty miles away, came into the possession of Major R. S. Dyott of Ludlow, and eventually was donated to the Museum of English Rural Life at Reading. Little is known of its history, except that it was built c1860. This waggon also had a crooked bed, but similar in lay-out to the Oxfords, and it had elbow standards of wood in the Hereford manner. There were mid-raves, one each side, and sixteen wooden spindles, set equidistantly. The body was straight in side elevation but the closed, flatly-set out-raves with eleven slim bolts to secure them and a forward projecting sill, hinted the influence of Clun, fifty-three miles away. There was also an echo in the shape of the head-board. It was identical with those built at Cropredy, near Banbury. There was a down-curved mid-rail, above which the sides were vertical, but turning under below it to a narrower front beam. The head was likewise set athwart the sides. The tail-board was panelled with spindles and hinged by pin-and-eye.

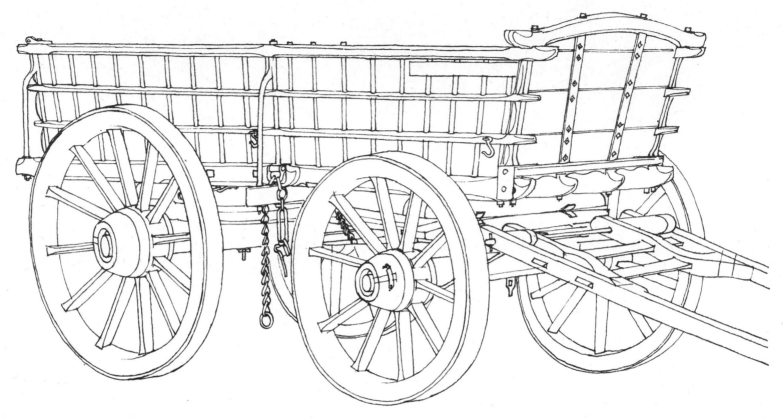

59 Derbyshire: Built by Bond of Mackworth, c1865. Body blue, under-carriage red. Out-raves absent. Carried harvest-frame. (*From a diagram drawn by David Wray*)

This waggon ran on broad wheels with diameters of 44in and 58in. The body was painted yellow and the red undercarriage had a longer than usual wheelbase of 81½in. The shafts were hinged by draught-pin to two hounds very well chamfered to a flat oval behind the bed. The deeply-dished wheels were spoked ten in fore and twelve in hind. The braking consisted of single-twist drop chains on both sides. There were no ladders but there was provision for corner-poles. The branding was indistinct, but was lettered in black directly on the panel board in front of the main standard on the off side. Not all Staffordshire waggons were yellow; there were others painted blue.

The waggons of Clwyd were also straight in all members but in all the details were distinct from both Lichfield and Mackworth. Some had no main-beam, others had. Some had five or six wooden staves supporting the sides, in addition to wooden standards; others had exaggerated cupid's bows at several points additional

to the wooden staves. Both these arrangements had two mid-raves on each side. The head-rails were surely the most ornate ever made and the makers were clearly out to make a good looking waggon. It was the more surprising therefore that the body was so high-pitched from the ground. Denbighshire waggons had cratch-like tail-boards.

Some waggons had narrow wheels, other broad, but nearly all were equally spoked twelve. The construction of the shafts was very complex. They were draught-pinned to four hounds and the pillow and bolster were both swelled to allow for the unusually large 3in main-pin. The waggons were equipped with short ladders and the owner's name was usually to be found on the head-rail. Some bodies had as many as fourteen narrow spars raked fore and aft. While blue appeared to be the most common colour, there were some in buff and others in yellow and the waggons were known to have been built in Denbigh, Ruthin, Wrexham and Llangollen. Many of the waggons had long-board floors suggesting a diverse usage, and the braking appears to have been confined to the drop chain, fitted on both sides.

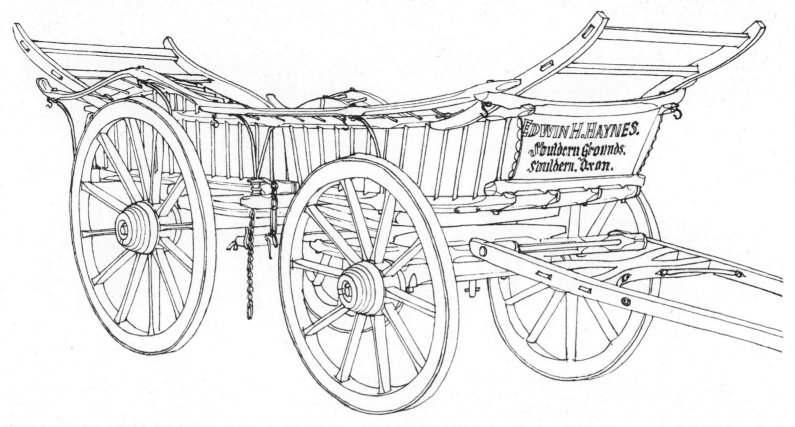

The Cotswolds, the Vale of Aylesbury and the Vale of the White Horse

In this considerable region, between Uxbridge in the south-east and Chipping Campden in the north-west, and between Edge Hill in the north and the Kennet Valley in the south, lies a vast complex of hills and valleys, divided by the course of the Thames. The greater part lies north of the river beyond which the Cotswold escarpment forms a frontier to influences beyond. From the Vale of Aylesbury there was a surprising eastward penetration into the Chilterns as far as Hughendon and almost to Uxbridge.

Among all the waggons in the region there was a marked uniformity. At first sight they had yellow bodies, with bow-raves over the hind-wheels and spindled sides, but at close hand several features became apparent. Most of them had their frames slightly indented, some more deeply so, and a very few had straight sides. The great majority had half-bows, while a large minority had full-bows, extending to the floor level. A certain number had bodies with a continuous sheer, like the side of a ship. Nearly half the waggons recorded had crooked beds with half-bows.

60 Oxfordshire: Maker not known. Body yellow, undercarriage red. Crooked bed and half-bows

A total of 202 waggons was recorded and these have been set out in Table 4 to show their distribution. The crooked-bed waggon, with half-bows, was the 'parent' design in the Vale of Aylesbury and the Cotswolds. The waist-bed waggon, with full bows, appears to have originated in Berkshire. The straight-bed waggon, with sheer-raves, was largely native to Banbury.

The relatively limited variation in design seems to suggest that the parent design, commonly called the Oxford, was generally accepted. As there were few plank-bodied waggons, the parent design and variations continued to be made after 1930.

The waist-bed waggon originated fairly late in the Vale of the White Horse as an improvement upon the restricted lock of the Wiltshire waggons, and it spread north of the Thames to the Woodstock district. Kench was building such waggons at Charlbury. They were commonly called Woodstock waggons, and had an indent or waist of about 11in compared with the 3½–4in of the crooked-bed waggons.

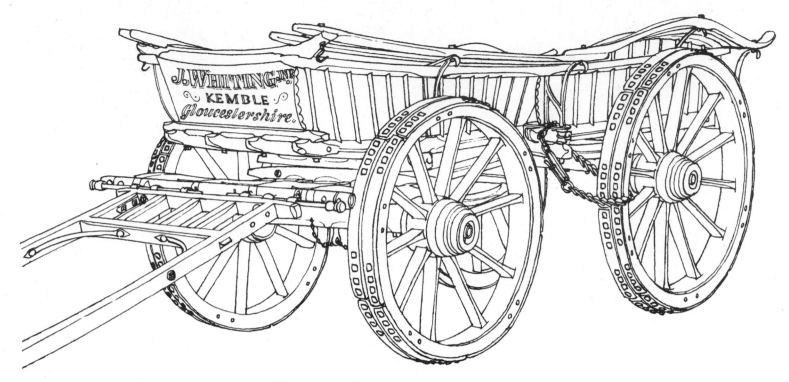

61 Cotswold: A hybrid between Oxford and Gloucester, built at Kemble. Waist-bed body with splinter-bar and broad wheels. Body yellow, undercarriage red

There were features common to all the variant forms. The broad wheel gave place quite early to the narrow, so that hoop tyres of 2½in tread on large wheels, fairly dished, became almost universal. Square iron gave place to round, so that by the last years very few waggons with square iron were to be seen.

The waggons were well built with a marked absence of the complicated construction which was notable in certain other regions. The tare weight was about 18cwt, some 5–10cwt lighter than many others. The waggons had a good lock and ran well so that they stood in high esteem. Any waggon with broad wheels, axle trees and square iron dated back well before 1850.

The great majority had only two hounds, hinged to the shafts by draught-pin, but a few, mainly in the Banbury district, had a splinter-bar hinge. Pair or double shafts were not known. The main-pin was usually inserted from the top, sometimes through the floor where three summers were fitted, but some makers, such as Long, of Aston, near Bampton, used the inverted pin. Almost

	Vale of Aylesbury	Mid-Cotswold	North Cotswold	White Horse Kennett	Principal Location	Totals	Percentage of 202
CROOKED BED:							
Full-bow	1	1	—	2	Berks	4	
Half-bow	48	24	13	5	Ayles/Cots	90	44.5
Sheer-rave	—	1	—	—	Cots	1	
	49	26	13	7		95	47.0
WAISTED BED:							
Full-bow	4	3	—	23	Berks	30	14.8
Half-bow	12	16	6	5	Ayles/Cots	39	19.0
Sheer-rave	—	1	—	—	Cots	1	
	16	20	6	28		70	34.65
STRAIGHT BED:							
Half-bow	4	—	—	—	V of Ayles	4	
Sheer-rave	—	—	32	1	North Cots	33	16.1
	4	—	32	1		37	18.3
Totals	69	46	51	36		202	

Table 4 Distribution and totals of variant designs

62 **Oxfordshire:** Built at Tetsworth. Body yellow, undercarriage red. Note full bows, waisted bed and square irons

without exception the wheels had ten spokes in the fore and twelve in the hind, but sooner or later one found the exception. One waggon, that I found at Denner Hill, between High Wycombe and Hughendon, had twelve spokes on all wheels, and was in company with another that was an oddity in every way. It had a deepish body, painted brown, which projected a bare 12in forward of the front axle line, with flattish half-bows supported by wooden staves. The body had only one summer and the tongue-pole extended back to join the hind crosspiece. It was built by Lacey of Naphill for Arthur Davis, who owned three other waggons of conventional design.

The felloes of the narrow-wheeled waggons were quite broad on the inner face at the spoke holes and were deeply hollowed between. The naves had a distinctive cone section on the nose. The fore- and hind-sides of the crooked bed were lap-joined with an overlap of about 18in securely bolted. The fore-side, or crook, was curved both laterally and horizontally, while the hind piece was straight. Some waggons had parallel sides while others had the

62 **Oxfordshire:** Built at Tetsworth. Body yellow, undercarriage red. Note full bows, waisted bed and square irons

sides a little closer at the waist. The iron standards at main and hind crosspiece varied in design according to the blacksmith's fancy, but it was to be noted that most wheelwrights used more than one design, making identification impossible on this feature. The majority of standards were H-shaped and many were N-shaped, all of them having the outer upright curved to support the outer rails. Over the fore-axle a V-iron curved similarly and there was a quarter iron above the hind-wheel to support the bow. Apart from the waggon at Denner Hill, wooden supports were not used on any waggon, except those made by Sumner of Cropredy, near Banbury. The outer rails projected about 11in from the top and in nearly every case were left open. Sumner, however, fitted closed raves, with panels called lime boards, and likewise Gerring of Milton, near Didcot.

With the exception of a few of the Berkshire waggons, which were spar-sided, the majority had spindles varying in number from ten

63 Oxfordshire: Built by Long of Aston, near Bampton. Body yellow, with red head; undercarriage red. Waisted bed and half bows.

to twenty-four with eighteen to twenty-one as the most common. There was no relationship between the number of spindles and the length of the sides at floor and top-rail. If a total of nineteen be taken as an example, these spindles could be variously disposed, from front to back: 5.5.5.4; 5.5.4.5; 4.5.4.6; 4.5.6.4; 4.6.5.4; and 4.6.6.3. At the two extremes, ten spindles were disposed 2.3.3.2 and twenty-four spindles were disposed 6.7.7.4. At floor the bodies varied somewhat in their measurements from 139½in x 48in to 142in x 52in with the depth at midway varying from 14in to 15½in. Midway the centre line of the main crosspiece was 1in or 2in nearer the front, with the fore-edge of the side 26–27in in front of a centre line of the fore-axle. With the spindles, as with the standards, there was no significance as to builder or locality.

The panel boards were not attached to the spindles but were lightly bolted to a series of vertical flat iron bars, five to eight in number and more or less equidistant. The head-panel was similarly attached. All head-boards were plain and capped by a robust and well-chamfered top-rail which was gently convex to support the out-rails. There was some variation in the tail-boards. Most had

oval-section top and bottom rails joined by seven wooden spindles and two iron rods, nutted at the tops, which were extensions of the hinge pins, which engaged eye bolts. Many of these boards were open, but not a few had a middle rail, slightly above centre and with a panel in the lower part. There were also some with conventional plank-type boards in one piece and barrel-hinged to iron straps that curved over at the top to end in forged rings to fit the rail ends. The common, spindle type was usually held shut with light chains. The plank had a sort of cupid's bow to the top edge.

Almost every waggon was originally fully braked either with roller or dog stick and the vast majority had small ladders which lay flatly at the top front between the out-rails and usually at the floor at the hind end. A minority in the Northleach district were equipped with corner poles to fit iron rings and loops. Rope hooks, fitted at four points on the out-rails, were of the free, swivelling type. Ninety-five per cent of all waggons had yellow bodies, a primrose chrome, mostly with yellow head-panels, but some with red, others with blue. About four per cent had Prussian blue bodies with heads of blue, red or yellow, and two waggons had all-brown bodies: one already noted, and another that belonged to William Taylor of Stratton Audley. The undercarriages of every waggon recorded were painted scarlet.

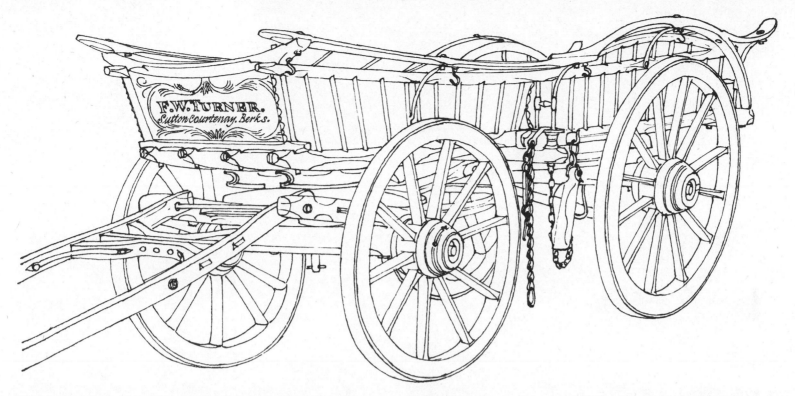

Chamfering was of a high standard but restrained, and there was very little lining-out or stringing. The lettering on the headboards was generally very good but without the elaboration to be seen in the East Midlands or in the West of England. The contrasting use of bold sans-serif, black letter and cursive was very effective with right-hand shading in a third colour. At the fore-end of the off side all details were 'written' in black directly on the panel board on both sides of the first spindle. The maker's identity was rarely shown, but Long of Aston fitted a long, narrow cast-iron plate to the head-rail reading 'LONG MAKER ASTON'. Gerring wrote his name on the fore off side.

Many waggons built in the Faringdon district had iron Y-standards, similar to the Wiltshire waggons, but further east, toward Didcot and Goring and again in the Kennet Valley, the standards were similar to the N and H types. The Oxfords were the most north-easterly of a widely disposed group with slight fore and aft rakes to their bodies, emphasised by their comparative shallowness. Sumner's waggons, built at Cropredy, might be considered hybrids between Oxford and Northamptonshire waggons that contained elements from both regions. They were straight-bed waggons with sheer-raves and middle-rails, with a turn under at the fore-end that was conspicuous, especially with the middle-rail across

64 **Berkshire:** Built by Gerring of Milton, near Didcot. Body yellow, with blue cartouche. Underparts of body red; undercarriage red. Waisted bed, full bows and closed out-raves. Note shafts set between hounds

the head. Sumner set his head-panels athwart the sides and some had splinter-bars to the hounds while others had the simple draught-pin. The lettering on the head-board was exceptionally good. The undercarriage, apart from the splinter-bar, looked 'Oxford' in design. Altogether I recorded about thirty of Sumner's waggons, mostly in the Banbury area, but a few far away. Fred Archer has one at Ashton-under-Hill (Bredon), another was noted at Goring and a third, branded 'Rt Hon Lord Vestrey', Stowell Park, was noted at Casey Compton, near Northleach.

The parent design, with crooked bed and half-bow, was extremely common in the centre of the region. It was as long ago as 1937 that I noted one between Stokenchurch and Henley-on-Thames. It was branded 'J. H. S. Fane, Well Ground Farm, Bucks', and was probably built by Clanville at Pyrton, near Watlington, or by Perkins of Chilworth. It was in conformity on all features with N-standards and nineteen spindles, disposed 5.5.4.5 front to back. The whole body was yellow with an open tail-board. Curiously there was no forward rise to the floor boards. The

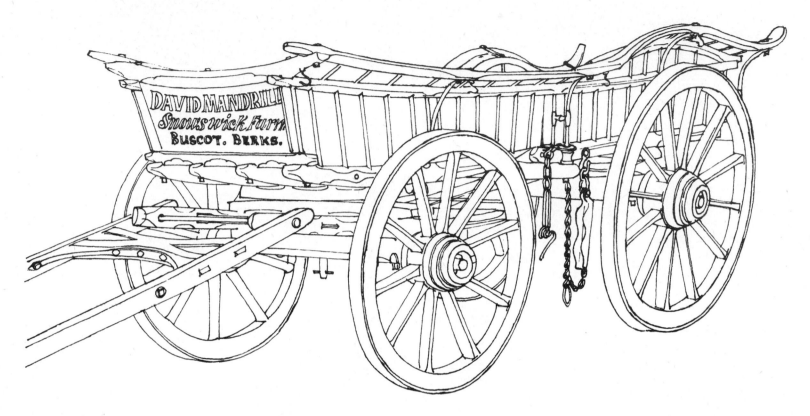

65 **Vale of White Horse:** Maker not known. Body blue and red; under-carriage red. Crooked bed, half bows and closed out-raves

main-pin was right way up. Well Ground is situated near Fingest in what I have always thought the 'cream' of the Chilterns, splendid country that takes you up to Christmas Common. This Fane waggon, like that at Denner Hill, was an example of the penetration into the Chilterns. There were others at Penn, Hughendon, Wooburn, Bix and Cowley (Uxbridge).

I noted a number of waggons made by Newport of Kidlington. They were among the best of an excellent family. One of them appeared in my first book. It belonged to William Kimber of Church Farm, Hughendon, and another belonged to Edwin Haynes, Souldern Grounds, Oxfordshire. Like the Fane waggon, they had N-standards but were differently spindled, the Kimber waggon being 4.5.5.4 (18) and the Haynes waggon 5.6.6.6 (23). The Kimber waggon had a plank tail-board with cupid's bow top,

but the Haynes waggon had a half-panelled tail, with spindles and a long-board floor (see Fig 60). A waggon made by Plater of Haddenham for White Bros of Sedrup Farm, Hartwell, near Aylesbury, had H-standards and twenty-one spindles, disposed 5.6.5.5. There was a spindled half-panelled tail-board and the fore-carriage had four hounds. This waggon had a long-board floor. In place of the usual writing on the off-panel, the name and farm were in white on a long black wooden strip, an echo of far-away Severn-side. This waggon was noted undergoing repair at Plested's shop, at Stone, in 1948.

Both the brothers Roadknight, who farmed in a big way, Sidney at Goulds Grove, Wallingford, and F. R. at Mead Farm, Thame, owned a number of waggons. Sidney had one built by Walker of Longwyck.

A Berkshire waggon with a crooked bed and half-bows was noted at Blunsdon St Andrew, between Swindon and Cricklade. It was branded 'David Mandrill, Snowswick Farm, Buscot' (near Lech-

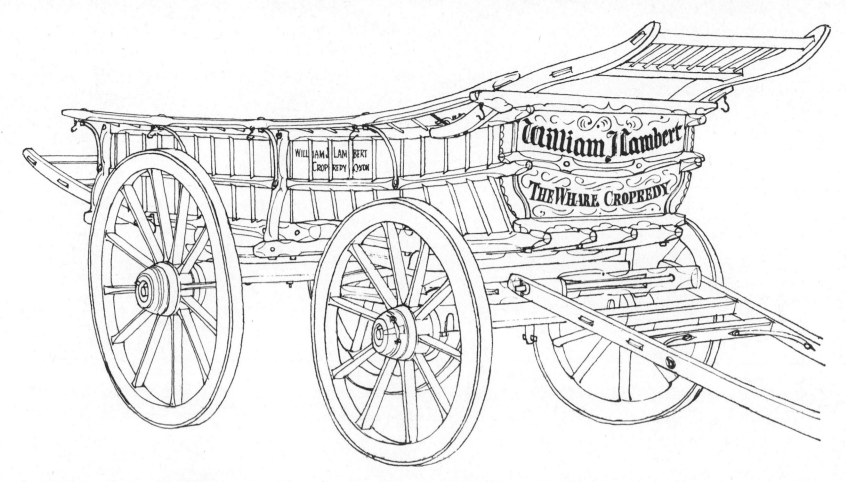

William J. Lambert
Cropredy Oyston

William J. Lambert
THE WHARE CROPREDY

66 **Cropredy** (Banbury): Built by Sumner in 1938. Body yellow, under-carriage red

lade). The body had H-standards and twenty spindles, disposed 4.5.6.5.

David Wray prepared a diagram, scale 1:8 of a waggon built c1860 and branded 'Percy John Read, Manor Farm, Boarstall' (near Brill). It was rebuilt by Bunyan of Brill in 1917 and repaired by Perkins & Son of Chilton in 1939. It had H-standards and seventeen spindles, disposed 4.5.4.4. The tail-board was half-panelled and the sides of the body were a little closer at the midway than at the hind-end. The main-pin was inverted. The Perkins at Chilton and Chilworth Estate may have been related.

Another waggon, branded 'Walter Fonge, Manor Farm, Water-perry' (near Wheatley) had square ironwork. It bore the last painting date, 1930. Some thirty waggons with waisted beds and full-bows were recorded, twenty-three of them in the Vale of the White Horse. Gerring of Milton built a number which were noted in the villages between Didcot and Steventon, nearly all with the shafts hinged between the hounds. Nearly all, too, had closed out-

rails, with the spindles varying from seventeen to twenty-two. A Gerring waggon usually had a blue head on a yellow body with the underside of out-rails and body painted orange. The lettering was contained in a cartouche. Notable among them was one for F. W. Turner of Sutton Courtenay (see Fig 64) and another for H. Pullen of Appleford. The standards were Gerring's own variant of the H and some waggons had all ironwork in a middle shade of blue. C. Day of Sutton Courtenay also made excellent waggons of similar design.

One other noteworthy waggon, made for C. M. Passmore of Moreton Hill, Tetsworth had square ironwork and twenty-three spars, disposed 5.6.7.5. Otherwise it was in conformity in all features (see Fig 62).

Waist-bed waggons with half-bows were more generally distributed in the region. Thirty-nine were noted in the Vales of Aylesbury and mid-Cotswold. Most of them had open raves, but a few had them closed and several had double raves. Some of the waggons built by Long had half-bows, some full, and Kench of Charlbury, whose firm must have been in business for a very long time, made some of his waggons with corner poles instead of ladders.

Not all of the waggons were yellow; several were blue, such as one for Roger Pilkington of Old Hinchwyck, not far from Stow-on-the-Wold. This had only thirteen spars. Two waggons with bodies deep enough to be sheer-raved were noted. One, a straight-bed, was branded 'W. F. Young, Fifield Manor' on a blue body and another, a waist-bed, was branded 'J. Shearne, Sapperton, Glos' and was noted in 1949 at Ashton Keynes in company with a half-bowed waist-bed waggon with double raves. This was branded 'J. Whiting Jnr, Kemble, Glos'. It was on broad wheels with shafts splinter-bar hinged. The standards were N type with twenty-two spindles, disposed 5.7.6.4 (see Fig 61). It was near Ashton Keynes that a waggon made by Long was noted in 1962. It was branded 'John Nicholas, Knowle Farm, Ampney Crucis, Glos'. It had H-standards and nineteen spindles, disposed 4.5.6.4 (see Fig 63). An unusual waggon, with corner poles and three summers, was noted near Notgrove. It had double out-rails with N-standard, but no iron stay above the fore-wheel so that the seventeen spindles were disposed 8.5.4.

The general lines, the shape and structure of the Oxford waggons appear to have changed very little since c1800. If this is correct then the Oxford as we know it, with the crooked-bed body and half-bow raves, must surely be among the oldest of extant designs. Some indication of its light draught may be gathered from the writer's personal experience when making a drawing of Mr Kimber's waggon at Hughendon. I wanted to move it into a suitable position and therefore picked up the shafts and drew the waggon several feet clear of the shed. At first unresponsive to my inexpert exertions, it then yielded and quickly gained momentum. I have had no comparative experience with other waggons but I feel sure that some were comparatively 'dead'.

Like all the older waggons, the Oxford was made by men who had 'grown up in wood' and understood points which are now no longer the concern of the carpenter. The great change, precipitated by economics, came when timber, from the moment of felling, was handled by merchants. The wheelwrights of the times before had gone out into the woods and selected their timber with an acquired knowledge which told them that different parts of the plantation produced different qualities of timber. They knew when to fell oak, ash and elm, and how long each required for seasoning. Much of

what Sturt wrote in *The Wheelwright's Shop* deals with this side of the business.

East Midlands: Northampton, Holland, Rutland, Bedford, Huntingdon

Long ago Banbury Lane was a 'drift', a way the drovers knew that went for miles across England. The present-day maps show it indefinitely, changing its status as it goes, but still striding away to Stamford. From the Golden Cap in Dorset, the Jurassic hills have seen three distinct designs of waggon, nearly all with bow-raves and shallow of body. First, the West of England, then the Wessex, then the Cotswold waggons. At Banbury the bow-waggons are quickly left behind, a fourth design appeared with the bodies much deeper, and after a variety of colours, orange all over became almost universal.

Even as far as the Fens and the Wash the design of these waggons remained very uniform in general appearance. They were orange in body *and* wheels, as remarked, though there were some variants from this on the margins of the region where some were brick-red, some blue. The unusual depth of body, being 24in, was emphasised by the double side-raves, roughly equidistant between top and bottom. There was a perceptible sheer with the hind-end slightly higher than the fore. There were two points on which all the waggons could be divided into north and south. South of Kettering the waggons had either straight (usually) or crooked beds (exceptionally) but in the Stamford—Boston—King's Lynn region the waggons had the lock-arch waist of East Anglian practice. The second and minor feature was the decoration of the head-panel. The waggons south of Kettering had a wheatsheaf motif each side of the branding, while those in the northern part of the region had the disc motif, containing the branding, except those made at King's Lynn. It was common practice to add the maker's name and the last date of painting. Phillips of Flore, near Weedon, went further and incised his name with date of building.

All the waggons had the head-board set athwart the sides. With the exception of those built at King's Lynn by Bolton, which had iron standards, all waggons had wooden standards with secondary wooden staves above the wheels. They were a little short in the body in front of the pillow and, with a number of exceptions, they had single, open out-raves further supported by iron stays. The head- and tail-board rails were gently arched and there were two summers. With very few exceptions the wheels were narrow, with treads of 3½in or 4in. Those made south of Kettering had ten spokes in fore and twelve in hind, but the remainder were spoked twelve and fourteen. Phillips' wheels all had tapered feet to the spokes, never tenoned.

All the waggons were fully braked and equipped with short ladders and throughout the entire region the attention to finish and elaboration in chamfering was very marked, while the lettering and lining-out was exemplary. My first encounter was at Helmdon, north-east of Banbury, where a waggon branded 'A. J. Gulliver, Helmdon, North(ton)shire', stood in Mr Gulliver's yard side-by-side with one from Cropredy, made by Sumner. The name of the maker, 'Phillips, Flore, 1910', was incised along the bottom of the head-board with the branding flanked by two conventional wheatsheaves. The owner's name was in bold white sans-serif letters, 'Helmdon' in black letter and the county in boldly serifed cursive. Pig-tails were fitted to each support and there were twenty spindles along the sides. The fore-ladder had two rungs with seven lathe-turned spindles between. The shafts were complicated in structure and hinged by draught-pin to four hounds and had inner elbows. The pin passed through all members and through turned

67 **Northamptonshire:** Built by Phillips of Flore in 1910. Body and undercarriage orange. Note detail difference between this 'wheatsheaf' waggon and the 'disc' waggon (*Fig 68*)

wooden sleeves between. The main-pin was inverted and had a chain-ring forged on at the bottom. The main standard was in twin form. This waggon ran on fairly dished 3in wheels, hooped and spoked ten and twelve.

A similar waggon by Phillips was noted near Canons Ashby and was branded 'T. S. Messenger, Adstone, Nortonshire'. There were slight differences in the single main standard and 3½in wheels. The shafts were hinged between the hounds and there were twenty-three spindles.

A third waggon, owned by William G. Barford, Foscote (near Helmdon) was likewise similar except for the absence of wheatsheaves and closed out-raves. The fore-carriage had a splinter-bar and the wheels were 3½in.

91

68 Northamptonshire: Built at Oundle c1845. Rebuilt. Oil-axles by Matthews. Last repainted by Stubbs, 1930. Built for service between Oundle and London. Entire waggon orange, lined black. Head-panel claret with green disc. Note crooked bed

Some of the waggons had 4in wheels and it was at Hardwick and Napton, near Southam, Warwickshire, that two waggons were noted, with blue bodies and red undercarriages, and a third blue waggon was noted miles away in the Vale of Aylesbury at Winslow, south-east of Buckingham. This waggon had only one summer and a single standard and was branded 'G. D. E. Wigley, Winslow'. Six miles east of Daventry, at Great Brington, a waggon belonging to J. Ashbury of Kislingbury, had been built by Fountain (of where?) and had broad (6½in) wheels, double straked. Two more, both belonging to Robert Bartlett of Radstone, near Brackley, were noted. One had a yellow body with a red undercarriage and the second, on 2½in wheels, had a brown body with a blue head-board and red undercarriage. The last example was noted still further away to the west of Stow-on-the-Wold. It was branded 'E. P. Brassey, Upper Slaughter, Gloucestershire'. It had 6½in wheels, *singly* straked. We may note, in passing, that L. W. Phillips were established in 1838 and are now busy with agricultural equipment. I regret that I have no records of waggons made by W. Ball &

Sons Ltd, of Rothwell. They owned the Royal Prize Works there and were obviously of considerable account.

At Benefield, near Oundle, I encountered the disc motif for the first time. I noted in 1948 a waggon owned by Phoebe Osbond, which had been repaired by C. E. Stubbs of Wakerley in 1930. The waggon was built before 1850 for road service between Oundle and London. The present wheels were very late replacements with 4in treads running on oil-axles, the caps of which were incised Joseph Matthews. They were spoked twelve and fourteen. The fore-carriage had the hounds splayed to carry a 72in splinter-bar, wide enough to carry two pairs of shafts. The head-board carried the disc motif and the treatment in seven colours was the apotheosis of the signwriter's art. On a deep claret ground, the disc was in bronze green, circled by a black border. The branding, the builder's name and date and the scrolls were in white, yellow, blue, red and green. All shading was left-hand. The waggon was in first-class order and the visual impact was positively breathtaking. The whole waggon was a rich orange colour.

The Museum of English Rural Life has a photographic record of a waggon near Fotheringhay. It had the disc motif on the head and a straight frame without lock-arch and was branded 'R. H. Capron Esq, Southwick Grange, Northamptonshire'. The sides

ALEX. WEST & SON
1940
HOLBEACH FEN

had a single main standard and usual secondaries. There were twenty-three spindles with a perceptible rake to those aft of the standard, and the out-raves were open. The waggon ran on 4in hooped wheels, spoked twelve and fourteen and hung on oil-axles. The single shafts were hinged by splinter-bar to wide-set hounds. The chamfering, lettering and lining-out were excellent. The main-pin was inverted.

The disc motif appeared on many of the waggons, but not all that had a lock-arch waist carried this device. In the region of the Wash many of the builders who had used the disc abandoned it soon after the Great War. Bingham & Sons of Long Sutton built waggons and carts for James Ruane and Sons of Rising Lodge, near King's Lynn, that had fine lettering on an elaborate ribbon scroll woven over the orange head panel, together with the date. Bingham also made a waggon for Alex West of Holbeach Fen. It was last dated 1940. This waggon had a crooked bed, with no lock-arch, the body was detachable (as most were) and the 4in wheels had twelve spokes in fore and fourteen in hind. Many of the waggons had staggered spokes. A surprise in West's waggon lay in the tail-board, which was spindled with only the lower half panelled. A further surprise was found on another waggon belonging to West because in place of the usual tailboard there was a

69 **Lincolnshire** (Holland): Made by Bingham & Sons, Long Sutton. Body and undercarriage orange

wooden bar which I had always thought peculiar to the Weald. But the head was set athwart the sides, which had twenty-two spindles. Another waggon made by Bingham in 1890 for J. T. and A. H. Piccaver of Long Sutton had this half-open tail, but otherwise conformed, with lock-arch and other details.

The disc was commonly encountered in Rutland and westward to Melton Mowbray to mingle with other designs of waggon, including the hermaphrodite, but, returning to the Wash, somewhere between Bourne and Grantham the East Midland design in its variant forms rapidly gave place to the radically different Lincolnshire waggons of Kesteven and Lindsey. Between the two there was not a single point of affinity.

Two waggons built by Bolton of Lynn were recorded at Castle Rising between Lynn and Wolverton. They were branded 'James Ruane and Sons, Rising Lodge', and were identical. They had short fore-ends and lock-arch waists. The sides had single mid-raves and seven spars (not spindles) supported by iron triangle standards. The head-board was set *between* the sides and the main cross-piece was massive, in the East Anglian manner. The under-carriage, too, was East Anglian, with a short splinter-bar on *top*

70 **Huntingdonshire** (St Neots): Body and undercarriage lined out black. Note staggered spokes and wooden axle-trees

of the hound noses. The 2½in wheels were spoked ten in fore and twelve in hind, with diameters of 48in and 60in. As the waggons were wholly orange one felt that the Boltons were casting their eyes in more than one direction when building. Jenkins, in *The English Farm Wagon*, describes the waggons of the region as Rutland waggons, but bearing in mind the extent of the region, which runs also down to St Neots and Bletchley, one may orientate the design between the Wash and Weedon. It was clearly a matter of prestige among the farmers of Holland that their waggons and carts were maintained to the highest standard. I have heard from several sources that when a farmer was going to market and knew that others would be doing likewise, the waggons, harness and horses were given the full treatment, as if for a county show.

In addition to the Northampton waggons there were on the farms of Huntingdon and Bedford some interesting waggons that were really hybrids between those of Northamptonshire and East Anglia. They had Northampton undercarriages with 3½in or 4in wheels, spoked twelve and fourteen, and hung on oil-axles, but in profile at least the bodies were East Anglian. They had lock-arches, a marked sheer and the sides were planked and supported by a single stout iron bar at main and hind cross-pieces. The closed out-raves were supported by six or seven iron stays. The head-boards were planked and with arched head-rails, all permanently bolted. They carried the 'spectacle' motif of this small region about the Ouse. Whatever notions some writers may hold about these spectacles, they could not have been other than pure decoration. In most waggons and carts this motif was recessed with the board therefore of double thickness. In a few cases of lately built waggons, however, the motif was painted on the board. These waggons usually carried the owner's name on the head-board. One such waggon was branded 'Hiam & Ruston, Hail

94

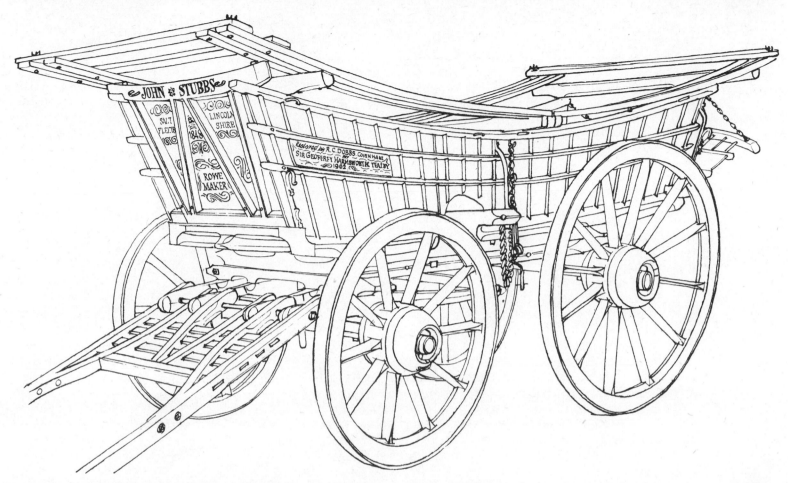

On the drawing: JOHN ✳ STUBBS / SALT FLEET / LINCOLN SHIRE / 1848 / ROWE MAKER / Restored by R.C. DOBBS COVENHAM for SIR GEOFFERY HARMSWORTH TEAEY 1962

Weston, Hunts'. This farm is near St Neots. In the two examples known to the writer, the wheels had the spokes staggered and were hung on oil-axles. There appeared to be some variety in the colours used—orange, blue and green. These Ouse Valley waggons were very short in front of the pillow and unlike the East Anglian waggons had the main cross-piece lap-joined below the sides. The fore-carriage was designed to carry a single pair of shafts hinged by draught-pin. These waggons were shallower than either the East Midland or the largest of the East Anglian waggons, so that the out-raves just cleared the hind-wheels. In the matter of finish, they could spring a few surprises. The Hail Weston waggon had the wheels fully lined-out black on an orange ground and in the absence of any decoration on the head the plank sides were elaborately panel-lined with continuous interweaving scroll along the length of the join between the two planks. The iron standards, rather to my surprise, echoed those of the waggons built in Lincoln by Cooke or Rainforth, whom we shall meet later.

71 **Lincolnshire:** Built by Rowe of Maltby le Marsh in 1848. Body and undercarriage orange. Note that all transverses are above the floor. Frames used for harvest; boards for roots, etc. Restored by R. C. Dobbs for Sir Geoffrey Harmsworth

Lincolnshire and Trent

In any district where two distinct designs of waggon were commonly found, it sometimes happened that there was a third design which was a hybrid between the two in that it contained elements of both. Thus in the Banbury district the Oxfords met the Northamptons, the hybrid occurred in the waggons made at Cropredy.

Factors of topography and land usage were not always decisive in determining designs and they were even less so in regard to two designs so radically different as the Holland and the Lincolnshire. The respective designs met on common ground with no physical barriers since the country was all fenland, with only the gentle wolds of the Grantham area running over to Louth. Yet the Holland variant of the East Midland design went no further north than Sleaford and Boston. The Lincolnshire waggons in the Parts of Kesteven and Lindsey were radically different, not only from the Holland waggons but from every other design throughout the waggon zone.

One's first impression of the Lincolnshire waggons was the high front, the pronounced sheer and the exaggerated rake of the head- and tail-boards. In their general lines there was a superficial resemblance between these waggons and the Conestogas of Pennsylvania. With the majority of designs of other regions the head-boards are decidedly wider than they are high, the proportion in some being as much as 2:1. But the head-board of a Lincolnshire waggon had the proportion of 6:5 width to height and the resultant height of the top rail from the ground was exaggerated by the absence of out-raves projecting from the sides. The waggon looked much narrower than it actually was. In one small detail there was another link with the Conestoga that may have been pure accident. This was the shape of the capping-plate on each fore-corner, strengthening the lap-joint between the fore cross-piece and the sides.

The waggons of Kesteven and Lindsey were among the large-wheeled designs with diameters of 48in to 52in in the fore-wheels and 60in to 62in in hind. They mostly had 3in hooped wheels, with ten spokes in fore and twelve in hind, hung on wooden axle-trees and set to a narrowish track of 62–64in over. All the foregoing features taken together may, or may not, have given rise to an apocryphal story about their proneness to overturn. In fact there was nothing in their proportions that would suggest a top-heavy waggon. R. C. Dobbs, a retired wheelwright now living at Donington-on-Bain, in a letter to the writer, expressed his opinion that an 'inheppen' (clumsy) waggoner could overset a waggon if the fore-wheel made violent contact with the body-sole. Any fully-laden waggon would be likely to come to grief in such conditions. In use on the road the Lincolnshire waggon, with its well-set wheels, ran as sweetly as any waggon. There is the less apocryphal story of the wheelwright who, having finished a particular waggon and being well pleased with it, picked up the shafts and drew it himself the several miles to the farm for which it had been made.

In common with every waggon built between Thames and Humber, these waggons had the lock-arch waist and shortness of body forward of the pillow. There were slight differences in the sides; some had a single mid-rave while others had double raves. All of them had the peculiar 'bipod' iron standard which had no outer upright because there were no out-raves to support. All the bodies had spindle sides, raked fore and aft, to range with the head- and tail-boards. The number of spindles varied from nineteen to twenty-one.

It so happens that of the existing waggons, those which have been preserved are all of very early vintage so that it is not known how lately the design was made. A fine example from Leadenham, now at the Museum of English Rural Life where it was restored, is one of the single-rave design. It is branded 'John S. Reeve Esq, Leadenham House, Lincolnshire, 1829' (in this case the building date). Leadenham lies between Sleaford and Newark. This waggon has a blue body with a stone (buff) undercarriage, and the shafts, with complicated inside elbows and keys, are draught-pinned to two hounds with the main-pin the normal way up but right through the floor-board and all transverse members. Another waggon, now at the Museum of Lincolnshire Life in Lincoln city, was a little younger but still built before the Crimean War, by an ancestor of L. M. Wright of Waltham, who restored the waggon to its present immaculate condition. Successive generations of Wrights were in business at Alvingham near Louth. This waggon, too, has a blue body but with two mid-raves and twenty-two spindles. The shafts, of similar construction, are set between the hounds. The name of the last owner, 'T. W. Shucksmith & Sons', is lettered in small black characters on a white panel across the head-rail, with the address similarly lettered on three white discs symmetrically placed on the head-panel. The shafts were very well made, with two inner elbows and a short middle piece all held by one main brace and three slim keys. A third example, originally owned by John Stubbs of Fleet Saltby, near Mablethorpe, was restored in 1962 for Sir Geoffrey Harmsworth of Tealby, by R. C. Dobbs, at that time working at Covenham. This waggon, built in 1848 by Rowe, had the body and undercarriage wholly in orange, which colour was confined to the coastal marshland east of Louth. The body had two mid-raves and nineteen spindles and a half-panelled tail-board. A dog-stick brake hung at right angles behind the axle-bed to which was attached a tool box. The undercarriage was generally similar to the other waggons, but the tongue-pole had two braces on each side and there were three summers. But the really interesting feature that distinguished the waggon was the position of the main and hind cross-pieces, *above* the sides and summers instead of in their usual positions below (see Fig 71).

One more waggon was noted, this being located in the Trent valley at Balderton, near Newark. It was built by Lumb in 1850 for Robert Atter. Like the Rowe waggon, it had two mid-raves and nineteen spindles and there were three summers. The wheels were similar, except that they were straked. It is likely that the other waggons originally had straked wheels. This last waggon was finished differently from the others, in brick-red all over. It looked very well, better than the drab 'plum' brown that was too much favoured elsewhere. The lettering and lining-out was in black, white and blue.

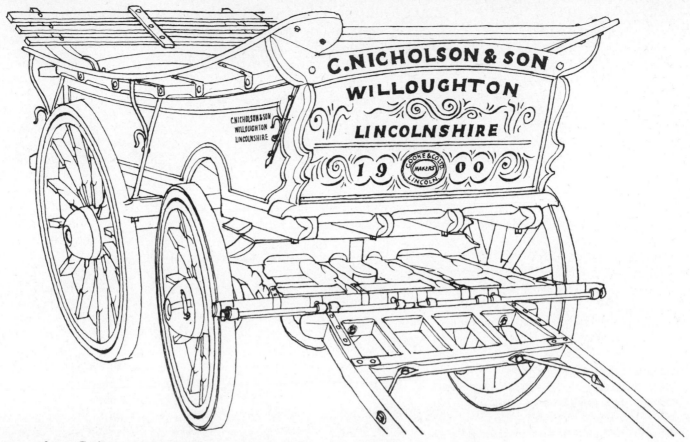

C.NICHOLSON & SON
WILLOUGHTON
LINCOLNSHIRE
19 00

C.NICHOLSON & SON
WILLOUGHTON
LINCOLNSHIRE

COOKE & CO LD
MAKERS
LINCOLN

Another waggon from Cotham, to the south of Newark, had a Prussian blue body and red undercarriage and yet another, from Sleaford, had a red body with a buff undercarriage, so it is clear that there was some local variation in the colour schemes. There also appears to have been a north-westerly penetration by the design into the Wakefield district of Yorkshire. Shibden Hall Folk Museum, Halifax, has a waggon with a blue body.

None of these waggons carried ladders, but they were equipped with boards all round. These, of course, were removable, with each side in two parts. In their place could be fitted all-over harvest-frames according to the kind of load being carried. One may comment on this similarity with the practice in Herefordshire, a hundred miles away. In fact the only difference lay in the names of the harvest-frames, because the 'thripples' of the Marches were the 'shelvings' of Lincolnshire. When one looked at these waggons it was the head-boards that really took one's eye. They had panelled heads with spars in the form of a W, with some very fine lettering and brush scrolls in all the spaces between. The name of the owner was lettered across the top-rail. The tail-boards varied a little, but all had spindles through middle-rails, some of them having the top space open.

72 **Lincolnshire** (Lincoln): Made by Cooke & Co Ltd, of Lincoln, in 1900. Body and undercarriage orange

In Lincolnshire the winds of change came during the middle of the nineteenth century, as in much of the West of England. They blew across the fens and the Wolds and in the city. There were two wheelwrights at work until quite recently making waggons which were a complete departure. Cooke & Co Ltd, and W. Rainforth & Sons, Britannia Ironworks, between whose work there appeared to be no more than barely perceptible differences. Both waggons had fully-planked bodies which retained the lock-arch waist and closed 'out-rung' raves. Their fore-ends were very well chamfered. The rather smaller wheels had 4in hoops, with ten spokes in the fore-wheels and twelve in the hind, flatly dished and set staggered round the naves. The wheels were all hung on oil-axles, which was a revolutionary change from the wooden axle-tree. The under-carriage had four hounds, all with the splinter bar, some of which were wide enough to carry two pairs of shafts. The Rainforth waggons had three summers while the Cooke waggons had two. One of the Rainforths, rather surprisingly in so late a waggon, had two pole braces each side. Both wheelwrights fitted the same design of iron standard at main and hind cross-piece. The colours varied, presumably according to the requirement of the buyers. Some were drab stone (pale ochre), some were a deep crimson, some orange and no doubt there was the inevitable blue one somewhere. All of them were panel-lined and very well lettered. Rainforth built one for T. B. Hutchinson dated 1944 that was standing in Bingham's yard during 1948. It had those curious 'Conestoga' capping-plates. It looked splendid, painted deep lake. Dobbs also restored a waggon for Rex Greenfield of North Cockerington, built 1909, and painted drab stone. In 1900 Cooke made one for C. Nicholson of Willoughton. The lettering and brushwork on the head-board was excellent. This practice of full lining-out was continued until no more waggons were built and it is to be remarked that the standard of the writer's art was constant through all the decades. Every waggon was a feast for the eyes and one was constantly aware of a pride in the job. Among both wheelwrights and farmers there was something like a mutual sense of status. Vehicles were regularly overhauled and were repainted at short intervals.

More examples of waggons are required before a final assessment can be made. A late example by Cooke was noted in 1949, near Broxted in Essex. This waggon, branded 'Edwin C. Pucks, Linsell', was fully-locking with small fore-wheels, and no pole, but with turntable rings. The four hounds were fitted with a splinter bar and the wheels, surprisingly, had twelve spokes in the fore-wheels and fourteen in the hind. The body was finished in blue while the undercarriage was red.

Yorkshire

If we closely examine those Ordnance Survey maps which show the land usage in the three Ridings of Yorkshire, we shall find that the largest county contains but a small area in which the farming is arable. A very large proportion of the whole county lies above the 1,000ft contour. It is part moorland, largely sheep pasture—a high, lonely landscape much divided by dry-stone walls where the solitary wanderer will encounter only sheep, red grouse and curlew. In the West Riding there has been a nearly overwhelming intrusion by industry and urban growth. In terms of waggon design, the remaining lowlands of the county may be divided into three sub-regions. There is the region of the Wolds, between York, Spurn Head and Filey; the Dales, north of York from Malton to Thirsk and west to Leyburn; and the Moors, a perimeter lying west of Whitby. Taken together the whole region constitutes the northern extremity of the waggon zone and in looking at the evidence, the waggons, one is conscious of this sense of extremity. Beyond this region, in Durham and the lowlands about the Cheviot, four-wheelers were never used, though even

there one might have run across the exception, probably built at Beverley. The type of farming on these uplands precluded the use of other than cart or sled. So we return to the lowlands of Yorkshire.

Both waggons and carts were generally much smaller than in most other regions. They were simpler in construction and more forthright in design, with a minimum of ornament. There was a comparative uniformity over the whole region with the widening estuary of the Humber isolating the region from the south. Except in one interesting feature hardly known on waggons south of the Humber, there was little by which an individual regional design was easily identified. That one feature was the centre draught-pole, which was retained on many waggons, indicating a very late use of pair oxen in yoke. (Oxen were last used in yoke in Sussex in 1926 and in collar in Gloucestershire in 1945.)

Many of the waggons had wooden axle-trees. This is less surprising because one had to go south of Grantham to find iron axles in general use. Many of the Yorkshire waggons had narrow wheels with hoop tyres, though there were exceptions in Holderness, with broad, straked wheels. The notable exceptions were those waggons built by Crosskill of Beverley, then already well-established as makers of steam tractors and cultivators. A Crosskill vehicle was to be identified by the name on cast-iron naves. Eventually they were to be found in many parts of the waggon zone.

All the existing waggons were built with straight-bed sides and plank-sided bodies and a great many had their fore-wheels small enough to turn under the body in a three-quarter lock, stopped from making the full turn by a tongue-pole. The wheels were flatly dished and the various wooden parts of the undercarriage were either quite straight or nearly so, with little elaborate chamfering. In a county where spring comes late, we expect a way of life in tune which left little room for superficial refinement.

The influence of Scottish design was often in evidence although some of the waggons exhibited a modest flourish in the structure of their head-boards. Far away in the south-west of England, Bristol Wagon and Carriage Works made what they called a Yorkshire farm cart, obviously intended for the northern farmers' attention. It had a pretentiously designed head and was designed to carry no more than 25cwt and, in a smaller pattern, as little as 15cwt. With oil-axles optional, it ran on wheels with 3in or 2in treads, according to the load. With detachable boards, the overall dimensions were consistent with the various sizes of Yorkshire-built waggons, most of which had wooden axle trees.

The smallest waggons were to be found in the Dales and were barely more than 96in long at floor by 36in wide and running on 3in wheels of proportionately small diameters, 26in in fore and

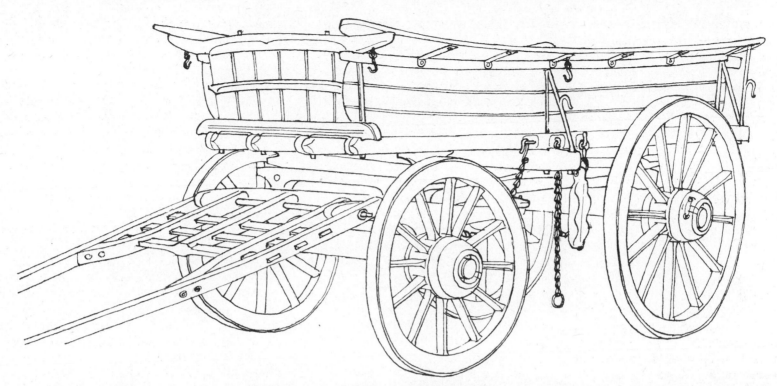

73 **Yorkshire** (Cleveland Moors): Made by Pearson of Egton, near Whitby. Entire waggon crimson, with pale blue grooves. Note wooden axle-trees

48in in hind. The waggons in use between Pickering and Whitby were generally much larger at 120in long at floor by 36in wide. They, too, were on 3in wheels, 38in in diameter at fore and as much as 56in in hind. But the largest were those of the Wolds, 144in long at floor by 38in wide, still narrow in the body by general standards. These, too, had small fore-wheels, 36in, but their hind-wheels were surprisingly large at 60in, and in proportion to the whole waggon they looked larger. The relatively small wheels were probably necessary for use over difficult ground where the horses and waggon were frequently turning corners. As elsewhere, the various measurements varied from one wheelwright to another in any district.

All the waggons known had closed out-raves, or 'everins' as they were called. My own first encounter with a Yorkshire waggon was not in the county at all, but in Suffolk, where a Crosskill, made for C. Wayman of Clare, was noted (see Fig 86). It was rather more elaborate than the foregoing will have suggested. There was a marked sheer to the top profile of the body, more to fore than aft. The plain sides were strengthened by seven quite robust wooden spars in addition to the support given by the iron standards, and they were nicely chamfered. The head-board had five similar spars all capped by an ornamental head-rail. As the southern maker had catered for the north, so here was a northern maker

supplying the needs of a southern farmer in the face of some hot local competition. It was noticeable that the body was not attached to the hind-end of the undercarriage, but it was stabilised against lateral movement by angle irons on the bolster against the side pieces. The shafts were attached to a four-hound carriage by splinter bar hinges and the tongue-pole was quite straight with single spreaders each side. The 3in wheels, which had twelve spokes in the fore-wheels and fourteen in hind, had cast-iron hubs with the fore-wheels small enough to permit a three-quarter lock. The body was blue and the undercarriage red.

A second waggon, which was shown in my first book, was made by Pearson of Egton, near Whitby, for W. Jackson, who farmed at Roxby. The body had the usual straight bed and a fair sheer to the slightly inclined out-raves. The general structure was in conformity, or so it seemed, until one examined the undercarriage. Of course, it had the expected small fore-wheels, but there was a considerable gap between the under surface of the fore-pillow and the top surface of the axle tree. This was made up, not with the more usual double bolster and riser blocks, but by a bridge-like bolster about 6in deep, each 'pier' resting on a hound about 8in

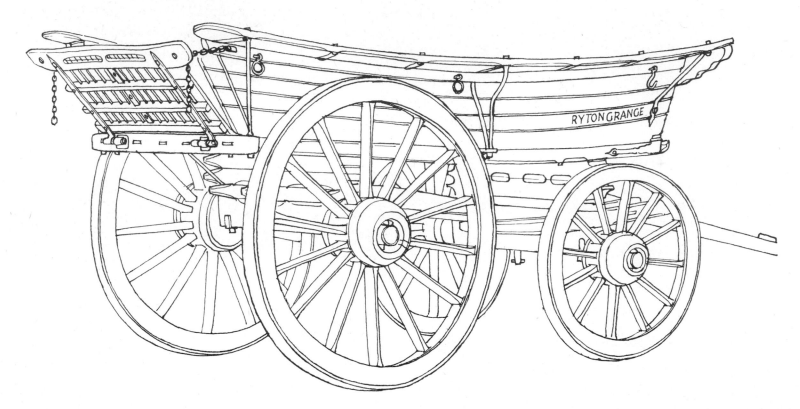

74 **Yorkshire** (Dales): Body ochre, undercarriage red. Built to take either draught-pole or shafts. Note wooden axle-trees

deep between bolster and tree and then tapering off rapidly to fore and aft. Between the hounds and above the tree there was a robust key. The nose of the tongue-pole was between the key and the tree and right through every member from top to bottom ran an abnormally long main-pin. Likewise, the bolt securing reinforcements to the arms of the axle tree ran through from the bolsters. The shafts, hinged by draught-pin, had flat inside elbows. The 3in wheels were spoked twelve on all four wheels and the entire waggon was newly finished in deep crimson with two grooves in pale blue equidistant on each side. The head had a slight curved mid-rail and five vertical grooves in the same blue. This waggon was in use when I saw it in 1951. I have seen waggons in the south that were infinitely more sober in their appearance.

A waggon recorded at Ryther, between Selby and York, had the fore-carriage designed to take a detachable draught-pole, and as built the pole could be removed and shafts, hinged by draught-pin, put in place. Like the other waggons, this vehicle was three-quarter locking and the plank-sided body had very wide out-raves, or everins, set quite flatly instead of being inclined in the more usual way. Both head- and tail-board were elaborately constructed with three flat spars, eight spindles and two mid-raves. The head-rails were very deep and had two oblong slots, each filled with seven thin rods. The entire head was constructed to be removed as required and there were three summers. The body was attached to the carriage. The colours, very much faded, appeared to be an indeterminate buff and red and the narrow wheels, hung on wooden axle-trees, had twelve spokes in fore and fourteen in hind.

Two more Crosskills were recorded, one built for J. L. Williams of Hopton Castle, near Clun, Salop, and the second for J. H. Thomas of Bockleton in the debated lands where Worcester obtrudes into Hereford near Tenbury Wells. This waggon was actually noted at Grafton a mile away over the boundary. The first waggon had plain sides, but the second had seven spars arranged

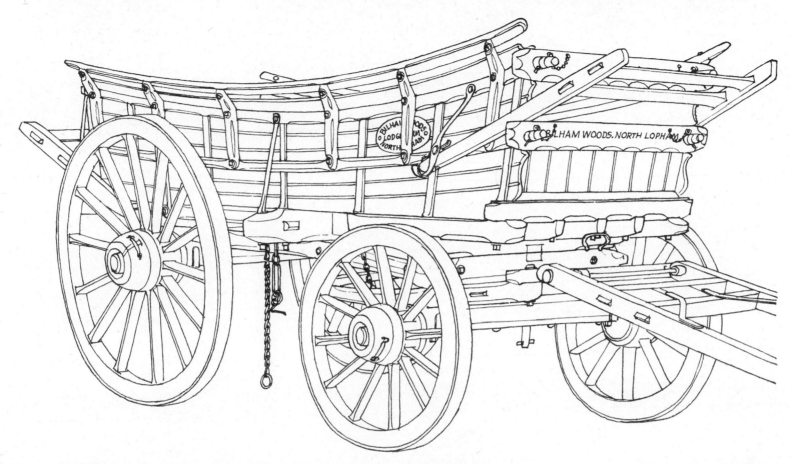

in a manner similar to the waggon seen at Clare in Suffolk. Both waggons had ochre bodies, but the Hopton one had no tongue-pole and was therefore fully-locking. Both had 3in wheels with twelve spokes in fore and fourteen in hind. The Hopton waggon had three grooves which were just discernibly blue. Both had flatly set out-raves, closed, with a gentle sheer. Apart from the waggons noted, which were painted blue, ochre or crimson, the body colour was reputed commonly to be brown.

The comparative absence of evidence of ornament in one form or another seems to conflict with Strickland in *A General View of the Agriculture of the East Riding of Yorkshire*, 1812. Much could have happened since he wrote, but he commented adversely on the excess of decoration at that time. It is not clear whether Strickland was making a comparative observation or merely implying a personal dislike of ornament. By the nature of the country, waggons could never have been as numerous in the Ridings as they were elsewhere.

75 Norfolk–Suffolk: North Lopham lies six miles WNW of Diss off the Thetford road. Owner's name on cast-iron plate. Maker not known. Body blue with white grooves. Body frames and undercarriage red. Wooden axle-trees

East Anglia, Essex, Cambridgeshire and Hertfordshire

The countryside of East Anglia retains its peculiar serenity in the face of progress and has a quiet that is not sleeping. The brown and green landscape that even today is three-quarters under corn, has no hills that are bold enough to thrust themselves at the sky. Yet you may stand atop Gog and Magog and look away to the distant Fens and when the light has that quality that Constable knew, then the chapel of King's College will become a clearly defined focal point, and it is at Cromer that one may watch the sun both rise and set over the sea in summer.

It was Norfolk that gave us the four-course rotation and Suffolk a fine clean-limbed horse. Today, too many miles of the quick-set thorn hedges, so carefully planted in the days of the enclosures (to the distress of John Clare) have been grubbed up, with dubious

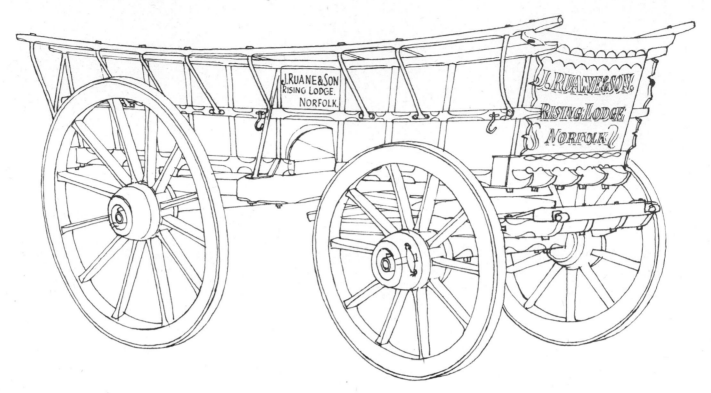

76 **Norfolk:** Made by Bolton of King's Lynn. Body and undercarriage orange

results, so that much of the country has a deceptively open-field appearance. Yet the composure so well interpreted by the Norwich school of painters is still there. It was in that scene that the East Anglian waggons harmonised so perfectly.

The waggons varied considerably in design and even more so in size, from the simply constructed to the more complicated and from the less than average size to the very large, the latter being typically represented by the waggons of East Suffolk. The name Large may be conveniently used as a generic term for all the bigger waggons that were made at Maplestead, Hadleigh, Brandeston, Westleton, Wymondham, Heacham, Ickleton and elsewhere.

With all the detail variations, from Cambridgeshire to Norfolk, the stress on the 'verticals' gave them the unmistakable East Anglian look. In spite of a quite marked sheer, the absence of any rake to fore and aft made them look 'static', devoid of any sense of movement. In the Large waggons especially the wheels were set wide and only slightly dished, making them stand four-square on the ground. The biggest were so big that I had to look up to them and their tare weight must have exceeded 25cwt by a fair margin. In nearly every case the whole effect was emphasised by the smallish fore-wheels against the comparatively large hind ones. The great majority had 3in treads. A few had straked wheels and

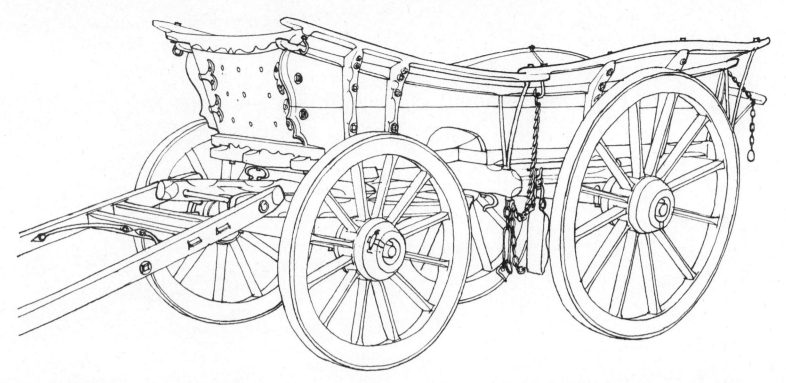

the broad wheel appears to have been given up at an early date. With the exception of the barge waggons built at Long Melford and Layer Marney, the body frames of every waggon, large or small, were built with a lock-arch waist that gave a very deep insection. The fore side-pieces, of angular timbers, turned sharply behind the pillow to a mortice and tenon joint in a very massive main cross-piece. The deepest had a waist of 14in. This was to some extent concealed by the one-piece side-panels, the lower of which had a large piece cut away to accommodate wheel lock. Inside the body all this was boxed in, making a considerable obstruction each side, a practice so long in vogue that it was accepted. Another feature peculiar to the region was the divided two-piece head-board, both parts being removable. The sides were mostly well supported by robust but simple iron standards with additional wooden staves, alternately of half-length and full. The massive main cross-pieces were about 6in square, tapering to their extremities. In a region of slight undulation, this weight was presumably of less consequence than it would have been in other regions. All the waggons were equipped with small ladders fore and aft. The fore-ladder rested flatly at the level of the lower rails with the tails held in ornamental iron rests. The hind-ladders fitted iron sockets at floor level. Such were the waggons built by Wood

77 **Norfolk:** Noted at Great Massingham. Very rare. Maker not known. Note bow-raves. Body blue, undercarriage red

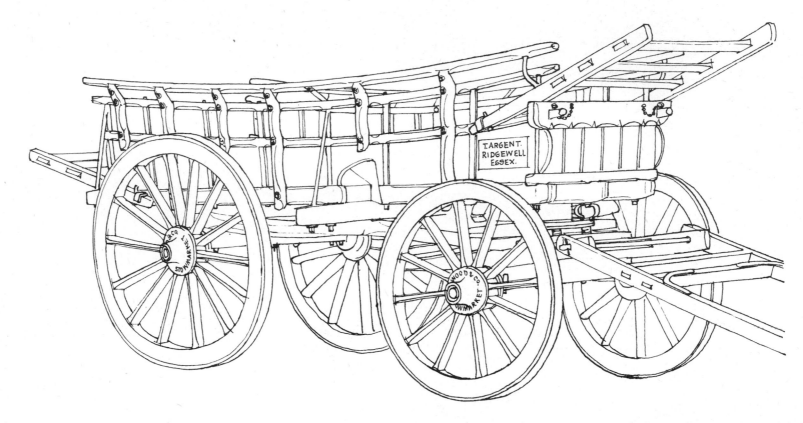

78 **East Anglia:** Made by Wood & Co, of Stowmarket. Body blue, green or brown, undercarriage red. In variant patterns according to maker. The most common type in the region

of Hadleigh. The Museum of English Rural Life has one which I first met in 1948 at Kersey.

A slightly smaller variant of the Large waggon was made by Scrutton at Brandeston and an unknown wheelwright at Westleton, near Dunwich. Their two-part head-boards were distinguished by relief scrolls, carved from wood and painted white on a blue ground. Both designs had the rails painted red. The fore-wheels of Scrutton's waggons were just small enough to clear the side panels, though the inturned frame was present. These waggons had turntable rings. The out-raves were closed, as with most waggons in the region, and set at a steep angle that made the waggons appear even taller. They were very colourful with red rails and staves and blue panel-boards and there was usually a grooving picked out in white. Another example was located at Aldham Hall, near Diss.

A waggon noted near Broxted, south-west of Thaxted, was

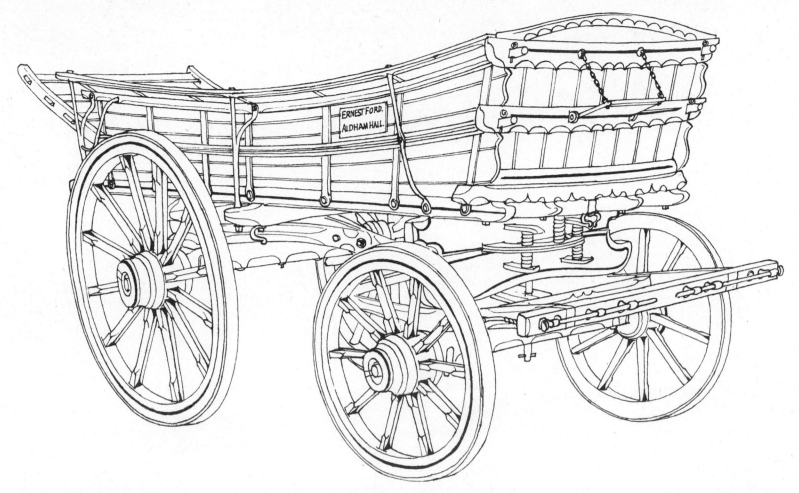

branded 'Foultains Hall, Ramsey' and set a puzzle as to location. There are two Ramseys, one too far away in the Fens and a second between Manningtree and Harwich, which was the more likely. In general lines it was similar to a Scrutton, but it had a lock-arch and larger fore-wheels. The 3in wheels had diameters of 47in and 63in and the spokes, as nearly everywhere in the region, were twelve in fore and fourteen in hind. The body measured 129in at floor by 50in, unusually wide.

Another, still within the family, was located at Michaelchurch Escley, in Herefordshire, under the Black Mountains. This had 3in wheels on wooden axle-trees. The sides had four red grooves on a blue body. On the off-side was a large cast-iron oval plate with letters in relief—'Bilham Woods, Lodge Farm, North Lopham', which is between Diss and Thetford. In its general lines it was not unlike a waggon at Heacham, near Hunstanton, for which David Wray prepared a full diagram. This was robustly built, both in the

79 **East Anglia** (Suffolk): Built by Scrutton of Brandeston. A three-quarter lock with tip-up seat. Body blue, with red and black grooves. Undercarriage red, lined out in black

80 **East Anglia** (Suffolk): Built at Westleton, near Aldeburgh. The relief motif on the head-boards varied. Body blue, with red or white grooves and motif. Note wooden axle-trees

undercarriage and the body, and had 3in wheels with diameters of 50in and 65in and hung on wooden axle-trees. The fore-carriage had turntable rings and splinter-bar shaft to both of which the East Anglian makers were much addicted. Essex, too, had a Large waggon, which could be distinguished from the others. One, recorded at Maplestead, a second at Sible Hedingham, a third at Ridgewell and a fourth at Layer Marney, had much in common. The first two had 2½in wheels on wooden axle-trees. All had blue bodies, except that at Ridgewell, south of Haverhill, which had red rails and uprights with deep green panels. The waggons at Maplestead and Hedingham had tip-up seats.

The Large waggons made at Ickleton in Cambridgeshire were quite distinct, with features derived from the Great Road Waggon built at Horseheath in 1780, an example of which is now in the Museum of English Rural Life at Reading. The farm waggon I saw near Saffron Walden was made by Godfrey of Ickleton for Henry Duke of Wenden Hall, Wendens Ambo, near Saffron

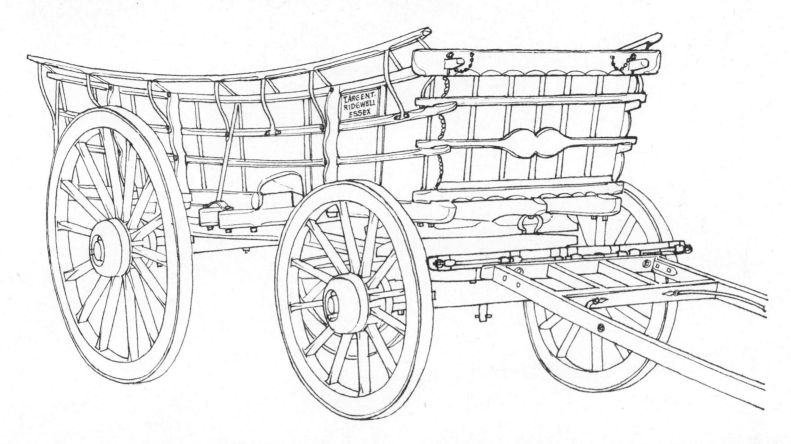

81 **Essex:** Built by Whitlock Bros of Yeldham. Body green, with red strouters and head-rails; undercarriage red. Note twin transverses and wooden axle-trees

Walden. This waggon was closer to the Northampton (and had it been painted wholly orange might have been still closer). It had the same easy sheer with two mid-raves and twenty-two spindles. The standard at the waist was twin, each on a slim cross-piece. It also had a straight bed with the sides slightly incurved. That the Horseheath waggon had a caterpillar-like humped bed at the waist suggests that the lock-arch did not penetrate west of Haverhill and Newmarket. The head-board was slightly bowed and repeated the sides in structure with only the top half removable. The open out-raves were supported by seven iron stays. This waggon had double shafts hinged by splinter-bar. The body was blue on a red under-carriage, but another, in Ickleton, was brick-red all over.

Throughout the greater part of the whole region of the four counties there were many waggons which may be called half-open, because the upper part of the body had no panel-boards. They were much smaller and quite plain, almost austere, with a head-board across the lower half only, which was removable. There

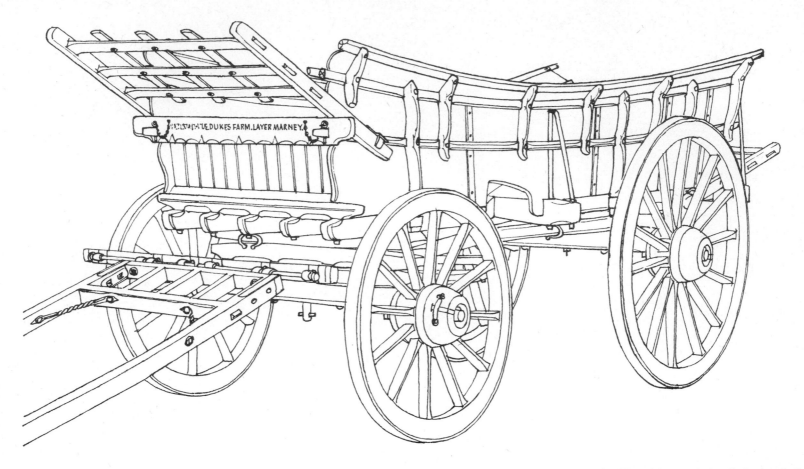

82 **Essex** (Layer Marney): Body blue, undercarriage red

were short ladders to fore and aft. The sides varied a little in their structure, some having wooden intermediate supports while others were wholly iron. The iron standards were very plain. The open out-raves were in both designs supported by a varying number of iron stays. Some had their wheels spoked ten and twelve, but most were twelve and fourteen. The dish was slight and of course they had narrow treads. The Half-open waggons seemed to be everywhere and were in fact the more numerous and accounted for thirty-eight per cent of all the waggons I recorded, with the Large waggon in second place with thirty-one per cent. Rather to my surprise, one at Edwardstone, north of Sudbury, had wooden axle-trees as did two at Willisham and Needham Market. Was the design of an earlier vintage than I had presumed or were those axle-trees survivors? All had lock-arch waists.

Cambridgeshire had a Half-open waggon that differed in having no lock-arch but the hump mentioned above. Without the structural weakness it gave a good lock with a straight frame and no obstruction internally. Henry Duke had two but he could tell

ROBINSON BROS.
TILLINGHAM.
ESSEX.

83 **Essex:** Built by Aylett of Tillingham. Body ochre, undercarriage red. Note the fixed head-board and the shafts set between the hounds

me nothing about their origin. Norfolk also had its variant design, with a straight-through bed and small fore-wheels that turned under. One, built by H. P. Smith of Morley, near Wymondham, was noted at Michaelchurch Escley in company with the Bilham Woods waggon. This was painted wholly scarlet. There was another that I noted in 1948 at Great Massingham, between King's Lynn and Dereham, that had been made by Crane who had shops at both Dereham and Fransham. This waggon, however, was in conformity with the majority and was painted green. Altogether these Half-open waggons were noted in every colour, but blue was by far the most common.

Southminster stands in the centre of that polder-like land that lies between the Blackwater and the Crouch. The builders at Southminster, Bradwell, Tillingham and Burnham retained the lock-arch, but having done that they apparently turned their backs on East Anglian practice to produce their own version of medium-sized, plank-bodied waggon and between them maintained considerable uniformity with no more than detail differences. All the

84 **Cambridgeshire:** Built by Godfrey of Ickleton. Body an ochreous red, undercarriage red. Note influence from Northamptonshire

waggons had a rich ochre and scarlet colour scheme. They had a fair sheer to the double out-raves and turntable rings to the fore-carriages.

Though King's Lynn is politically within Norfolk, Bolton, who built there, was clearly orientated towards the Wash and his waggons have been dealt with under East Midlands. But in that part of the county lying north of Swaffham, a distinctive Norfolk waggon was built. The body was so very short in front of the pillow that the waggon looked tail-heavy. It had quite large fore-wheels for which the lock-arch was retained. The body had a good sheer, rising well to fore. Unlike most waggons in the region, the Norfolk had a lap-jointed main cross-piece. The out-raves were closed and just cleared the hind-wheels, but one waggon noted at Great Massingham had a shallow body with the hind part bowed over the wheels, which were equally spoked twelve all round. Both Crane at Fransham and Cresswell at Narborough made the Short Norfolk.

At the turn of the century and later, a number of wheelwrights at Long Melford, Stowmarket and Layer Marney were building a plank-bodied waggon that had a three-quarter lock because the pole was retained. These may be considered as barge waggons. They were departures from the earlier designs but managed to retain the essential points, such as short ladders and short splinter-bars, but had fixed head-raves and plank-raves. The sides were entirely planked. Most had blue bodies but there were other colours. The builders were two at Melford, Silver and Ward; Wood & Son of Stowmarket, and Howard of Layer Marney.

Over the whole region there was a good range of colours without local significance, except for ochre in the Southminster district and orange in King's Lynn. Of the total, sixty per cent were blue, fifteen per cent green, fourteen per cent ochre and just over four per cent brown. Among the remaining six per cent were orange, yellow, red and white. Except for the King's Lynn waggons all had scarlet undercarriages. A not insignificant detail, yet one easily overlooked, was the curious rope hook, two-pronged with the prongs facing and fitted under the front cross-piece. Almost every waggon had one. There was a marked absence of the branding that was proudly emblazoned on so many waggons with only an unobtrusive black rectangular plate inscribed in white letters, on

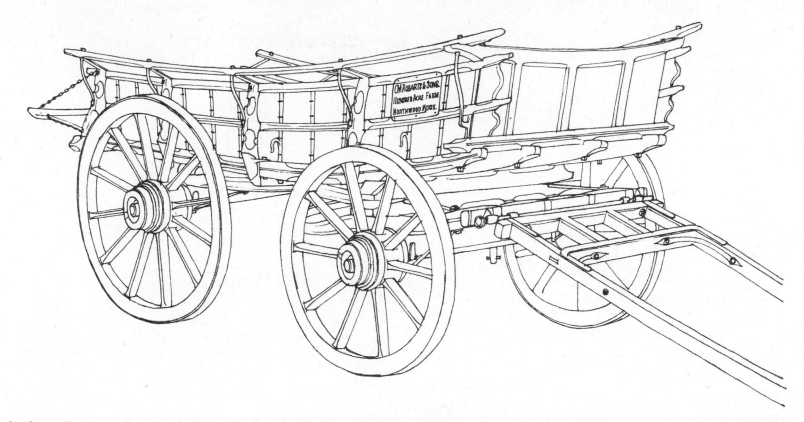

the fore off side. A few wheelwrights fitted makers' plates, usually on the head.

H. R. Waiting appears to have been in doubt as to whether there was a distinct Hertfordshire waggon. In the last years there were wheelwrights active at Bovingdon (W. J. Brown), Welwyn (Meadcroft), Hertford (Raymond), Braughing (Bysouth), Barley (W. Casbon) and another at Harpenden, all making waggons that were collectively to be regarded as westerly variants of other designs, resulting in several cases as hybrids. Bysouth was lately making prize-winning tip-carts and may well have made waggons at one time. Casbon, at Barley, near Royston, was well out on the fringe, looking towards Cambridge.

A waggon I saw at Kimble, near Risborough, had no place in the Vale of Aylesbury. It was not a large waggon and its smallish wheels were just large enough for it to be a quarter-lock. The body was fairly shallow with a very easy sheer. There was no mid-standard, as such, only a strouter like those above the axles. It was fully panelled, with mid-raves, and the out-raves were supported by five iron stays, the foremost of which might have come off a Wiltshire. Along the side there were twelve spindles to which the sides were laced, three of which were of iron with forged-on

rope hooks. The head-board had eight spars and a concave rail. The tail-board was similar with three barrel hinges. The hind standard and the three strouters were so exquisitely chamfered they could have come off a century-old Dorset, and they were held by deep iron sockets. The hounds had cyma curves, as on a Clun, but were capped with a short splinter-bar to take single East Anglian shafts. The wheels were narrow of tread, hooped and spoked ten in fore and twelve in hind. The waggon body was blue with a maroon interior and the undercarriage was red. It carried no branding, except for a black rectangular plate on the off side at the fore-end. This was inscribed 'C. M. Robarts and Son, Hundred Acre Farm, Northwood, Mddx'. To this day the waggon has remained a mystery unsolved. Had I found it in Dorset, without inscription, I would have accepted it as a Dorset, albeit rebuilt.

Eastward from Harpenden the waggons assumed East Anglian features. One noted at Harpenden hinted at Ickleton and Horseheath, even though those villages were far away with all the country about Stevenage between.

5 Trolleys, Hermaphrodites and Boat-waggons

The trolley came into use during the latter part of the eighteenth century mainly, it seems, in Herefordshire, but also in Shropshire, Cheshire, Worcestershire, and Radnorshire. Some of them ran on narrow wheels but since the trolley originated in Herefordshire it would have taken on the features of its 'big brother', especially the broad wheels. In Chapter 1 the Trolley is defined as a harvest frame running on four wheels. One, in excellent condition, was noted at Aymestrey Court, near Wigmore, and was owned by Mr Tedstone. The frames were unusual in having hinged ends which stood upright in the open position and when folded flat shortened the overall length, but mainly they served to contain the load better. This vehicle ran on large, broad wheels, doubly straked (see Fig 93).

Another, built by Francis of Newcastle-on-Clun, had 3in straked wheels. The shafts were hinged by a draught-pin to the four hounds, which had the typical cyma curves to fore and aft of the crossing and the carriage also had the inverted type of main-pin with cone and ring head (at the foot). The narrow wheels were quite deeply dished and spoked ten in fore and twelve in hind and, as with all trolleys, were braked only by drop chains, one on each side.

A third Trolley was noted opposite the writer's house. This one had a lower floor, at the normal waggon floor height, whereas nearly all trolleys had the floor on risers, setting it clear of the hindwheels. It also had the normal main and hind cross-pieces, serving no purpose. This suggested a possible conversion from a waggon. The shafts were draught-pinned to four hounds that were

much straighter than usual for the region. The broad, straked wheels were hung on wooden axle-trees. They had diameters of 48in and 56in, standard for the county, set on a track of 68in over. The normal drop chains were fitted on both sides with cleats on the hind-wheels. The lock-chains ran from fore- to hind-bolster, with suspension at three intermediate points (see p 28). This trolley was built by Lewis of Yarkhill and owned by S. Harper.

The Hermaphrodite appeared to have been unevenly distributed between Rugby, Lindsey and Norfolk and was not commonly to be encountered, although I recorded five in Warwickshire. They were located at Pailton, Stretton-under-Fosse (see Fig 92). Harborough Magna and Monks Kirby, near Rugby. All were finished buff. Another, owned by Sir William Cook of Wyld Court, Hampstead Norris, Berkshire (near Newbury), had actually been made at Tetford, north-east of Horncastle. It had wooden axle-trees and the W-panelling on the cart head-board was distinctive of Lincolnshire. Apart from the iron axles on the examples near Rugby, there was little difference in the general structure.

Boat-waggons became very common over the greater part of south-western England, more so in some counties than in others (see Fig 91). It was noticeable that this unusually shallow-bodied waggon did not find favour in those parts where the deeper-bodied designs were accepted. Inevitably there were exceptions to this as in everything else.

Among the many makers were Cottrell Rose at Hungerford; W. Tasker at Andover; H. J. and W. Wilder at Wallingford; E. and H. Roberts at Deanshanger, Stony Stratford; Barrett at

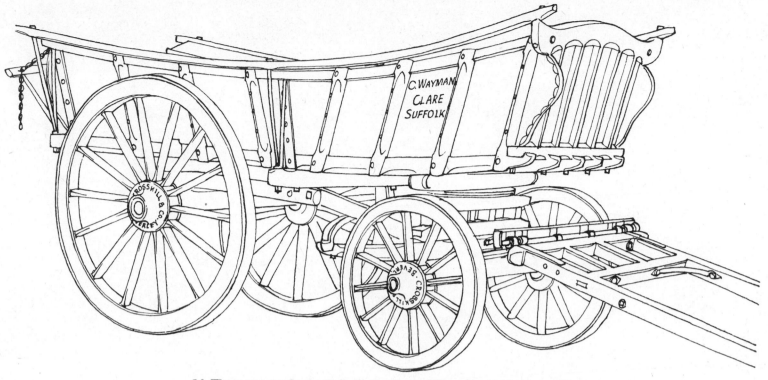

86 Three-quarter Lock: Built by Crosskill of Beverley. Body blue, under carriage red. Although made for East Anglia, the Yorkshire design was retained

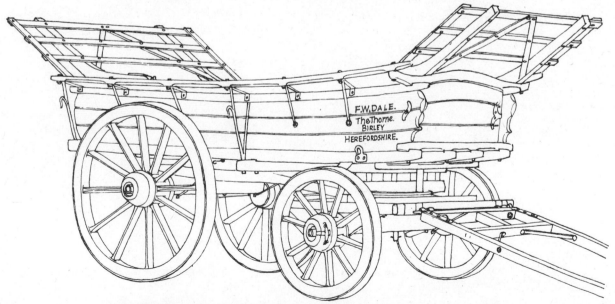

87 Three-quarter Lock (Bromsgrove): Built by Daniel Giles c1897. Body yellow

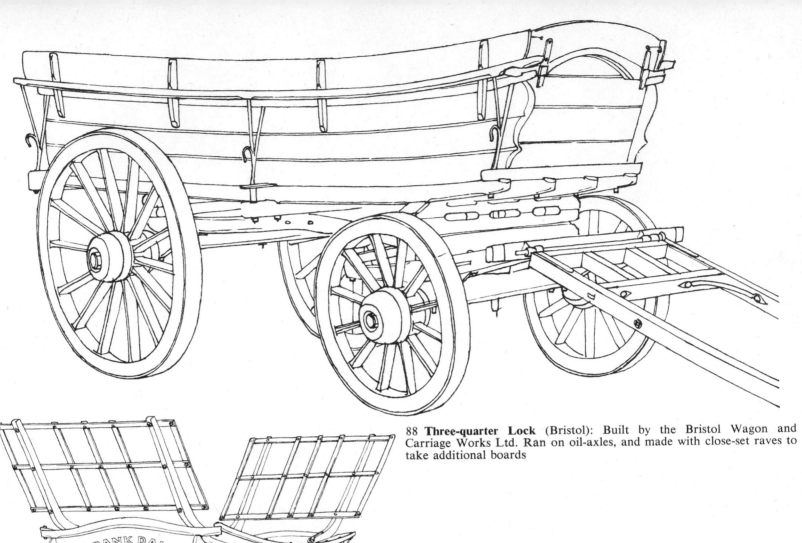

88 **Three-quarter Lock** (Bristol): Built by the Bristol Wagon and Carriage Works Ltd. Ran on oil-axles, and made with close-set raves to take additional boards

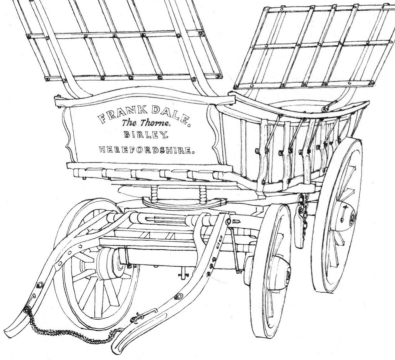

FRANK DALE.
The Thorne.
BIRLEY.
HEREFORDSHIRE.

89 **Three-quarter Lock** (Devon): Built by Hensley of Exmouth, c1890. Body blue, undercarriage red.

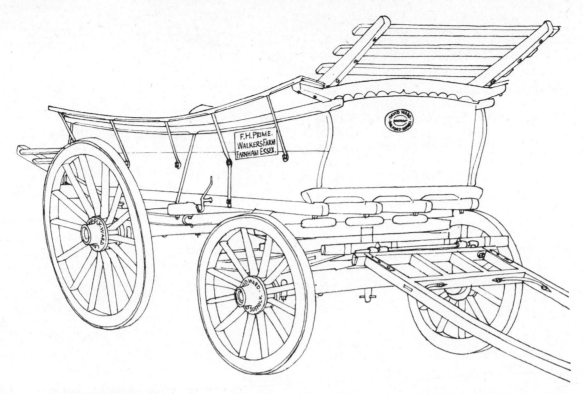

Wroughton, Swindon; the Bristol Wagon and Carriage Works and rather surprisingly Jones at Llangattwg, Monmouth, together with others unnamed. With little more than detail variations from one to another they were surprisingly similar. It was as though they were variants of a standard design. Many of them had cast-iron hubs and one or two actually had axle-trees. All had small wheels, usually 36in in fore and 50in in hind with treads usually of 3in. They all carried the large upright ladders that originated in Wiltshire and all of them were fully braked. Wilder made one for Evan Jones of Dinedor, Hereford, distinguished by a red panel on a black head-board. The makers wrote to me that they never used the term 'Boat' but called their product the 'Patent Steel Framed Waggon'. A plate of cast-iron on the side so described it. The waggon made at Llangattwg was for R. and L. Francis of Garway Court and it was quite straight in sheer with each side in one piece. Another, by Barrett for Clayton Wheeler, was finished in blue with yellow panelling. The undercarriage was orange and altogether the waggon was very colourful. D. R. Kinch of Church Farm, Inglesham, seems to have been something of a collector. He owned one waggon from Brecon, an Oxford, a Wiltshire and two Boat-waggons. One, built in 1910 by Rose, was all black on the body and with framework and undercarriage in scarlet, all

90 **Three-quarter Lock** (Suffolk–Essex): Made with variations of detail by David Ward; Silver of Long Melford; and Howard Bros of Layer Marney. Body blue, undercarriage red

lined out in white and yellow. The second Boat, made by Tasker, was similar but with blue body.

It was during 1948, while I was wandering in the Vale of Aylesbury, that I found a Boat-waggon undergoing repair in a wheelwright's yard at Grendon Underwood, between Aylesbury and Bicester. I noted the maker's name on the iron hubs, 'Rose, Hungerford', but in curiosity I asked the wheelwright what he called this waggon. 'We call this a Berkshire', he replied. It was at Brill, not far away, that I heard the Oxford waggon called a 'Cherrypicker'. I make no comment here, on these vernacular usages.

Bristol Wagon and Carriage Works Ltd, an associate of Leeds Forge, who made some cars for *wagon-lits*, made Boat-waggons and called them so. Like Crosskill, they made everything and catered for regional trends, so that a Bristol vehicle was not recognised as such until one looked at the cast-iron hubs or the caps on the oil-axles. Among a number of Bristols noted there was one at Winson, near Bibury, owned by Samuel Perry, which had a yellow body, and another at Burghill, near Hereford,

115

belonging to W. L. Jones. This one, in blue, closely followed the lines of a Hereford and had a salmon undercarriage. There was a third in Kent at Flimwell, near Goudhurst, owned by Brett, but this conformed to no county, certainly not Kent. Bristol even made a bow-raved 'Gloucestershire' waggon complete with cow-horn head. It was available in two sizes, to carry 1½ tons on 2¼in wheels and—a two-horse waggon—to carry 3 tons on 4½in wheels. Bristol made vehicles of every description, for export as well as the home market. All their products were made on quantity production.

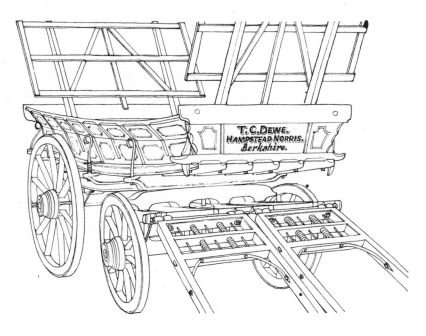

91 **Boat-waggon** (Hungerford): Built by Cottrell Rose of Hungerford. Body blue, with white or red lining-out; undercarriage red, with black or yellow lining. No turntable rings

Map 2 Distribution of types of cart. Continuous arrows indicate influences. The boundary between the Eastern or Scotch Cart and the Western or Butt Cart can only be approximate since intrusions and inconsistencies occurred in many places.
Many tip-carts coexisted with the regional designs of waggon. The various designs of non-tipping harvesting cart were each peculiar to a region

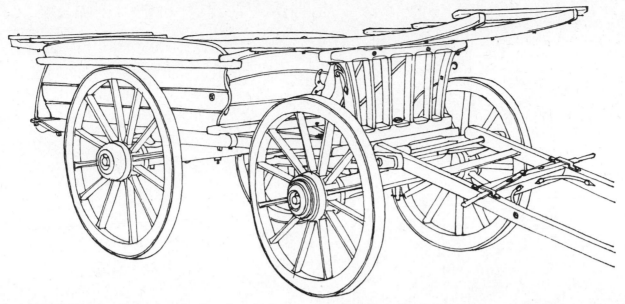

92 Hermaphrodite (Warwickshire): Stretton-under-Fosse, near Rugby. Body yellow, remainder red

93 Trolley (Herefordshire): From Aymestrey, c1800. Framework blue, undercarriage salmon. Note folding ends (not usual practice)

6 Tip-carts

According to regional usage, tip-carts were variously known as tumbrels, trumbels, Scotch carts and butt-carts, etc. They all had hinged bodies, with locking devices which, when released, allowed the body to be tipped on the hinges to discharge their loads, and they were made in a variety of designs. On large farms they were principally used for the conveyance of manure in winter, but many were designed to carry hay or corn. Until recently Bingham & Sons of Long Sutton, Lincolnshire, made a Scotch cart which had drop-sides as well as tail for access to either side as necessary. This cart ran on rubber-tyred artillery wheels and appeared to represent the final development. While the terms 'butt', 'moss', 'box', 'dobbin' and 'trumbel' were clearly regional in origin, the term 'Scotch' does require some clarification.

During the latter part of the last century a considerable number of Scottish farmers left their homeland and came south with their families, their livestock and equipment to take farms in East Anglia which were being let at low rents during the agricultural depression, rather than allow the land to deteriorate for want of cultivation. A secondary result of this migration was the introduction to East Anglia of the type of cart used between Ayrshire and Aberdeen. We do not know precisely the actual extent of the area to which the Scots came, nor do we know by what route they came. There were two likely routes from Ayrshire and Galloway. One through Carlisle, Appleby, Bowes, York and Brigg down to Spalding, and the second by Kendal (a droving centre), Skipton and York. Once the farmers were established the eventual result was the general acceptance of the cart in the region.

We may presume that the English farmers of the counties north of the Humber were familiar with the Scotch cart long before the exodus. It must have been a better design than the East Anglian because the demand could not be met locally, so that large numbers were bought from Scottish wheelwrights. Inevitably the influence spread further inland and the term 'Scotch' must be dated from this time since it would hardly be accepted among the Scottish farmers and wheelwrights. Since the word 'tumbrel' or 'tumbril' dates from 1440 OED we appreciate that 'Scotch' meant more than Scottish. It meant a type.

In the course of two comparatively recent cycling tours in Scotland I came across very few carts, but by way of compensation an excellent example was noted at North Strome in Wester Ross, a long and difficult way from Ayrshire (see Fig 99). It was different from the Scotch cart as accepted, having a body of medium depth and detachable boards all round. The tip action was locked by a simple clip instead of either the strap stick or the sword, and the boards were not fixed but detachable. The 3in wheels, tyred with hoops, had a diameter of 48in with twelve spokes. The cart had recently been made, going by its condition, and had since been repainted. All the framework was viridian with red plank sides and head. Wheels and shafts were red and the wheels had van-type naves. This cart appeared to be Scottish rather than Scotch. What was the distribution of the Scotch cart in Scotland?

A common practice on many Scottish farms at hay-time was to 'stook' the hay on tall wooden tripods which had been set out in rows in the fields. When the hay was dry, the laden tripods were

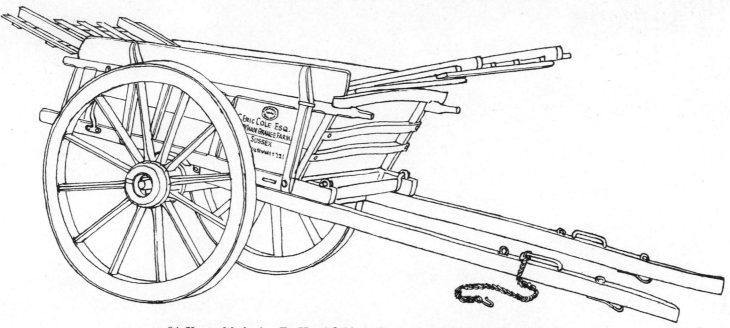

94 **Kent:** Made by F. Heathfield & Sons of Ashford. Body cream, wheels, shafts and ladders red. Body locked by strap-stick

95 **Essex:** Built by Whitlock Bros, Yeldham. Body green, wheels and shafts orange. Body locked by sword and lever. No ladders

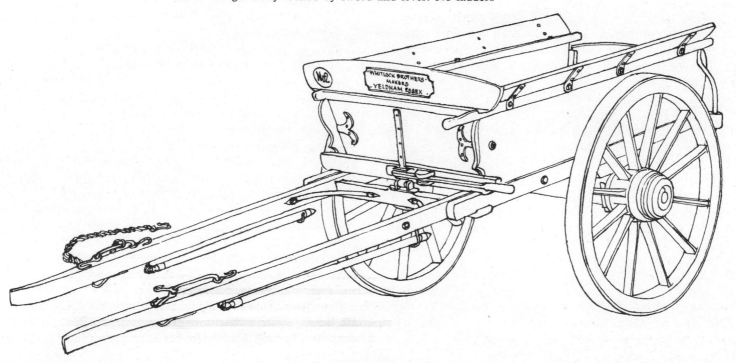

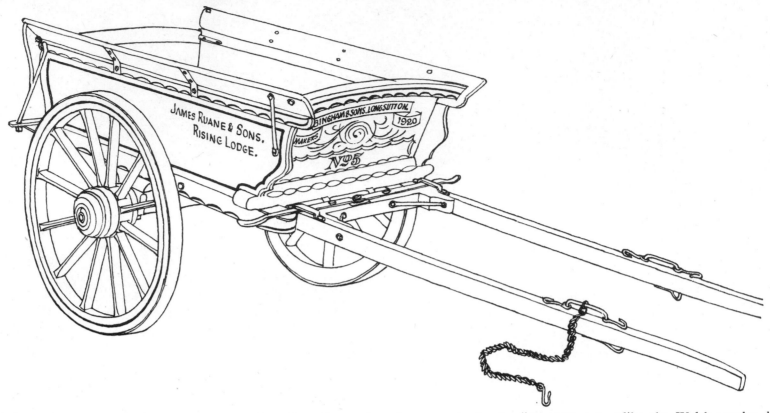

96 Lincolnshire (Holland): Made by Bingham & Sons, Long Sutton, in 1920. Body, wheels and shafts orange, lined out in black, green and white. Body locked by lever

drawn on to low-loading carts not unlike the Welsh gambo, but with tipping platforms. Under a full load the platform returned to its normal position. On many of the upper hillside farms, sleds were used for the same purpose and on some farms the Long-cart, similar to the Welsh long-cart, was also widely used.

In the eastern half of England, south of the Humber, carts were generally larger than those in the western half, but size alone was not the deciding factor in distinguishing the one from the other. The eastern carts usually had the axle-bed bolted to the body to which the shafts were hinged, while the western had the shafts bolted to the bed, above which the body was hinged. The eastern carts were mostly deeper in the body and almost invariably had permanently fixed boards and were usually equipped with quite large fore- and aft-ladders. This last indicated the use of carts at harvest in addition to waggons. The fore-ladder extended flatly forward over the shafts on which it was supported by sticks. Such carts could carry as much as the hermaphrodite, which may be considered as deriving from the Scotch cart.

Very few western carts carried ladders, but were equipped with removable boards, similar to those on waggons so equipped. The carts were generally smaller, but of course there were exceptions

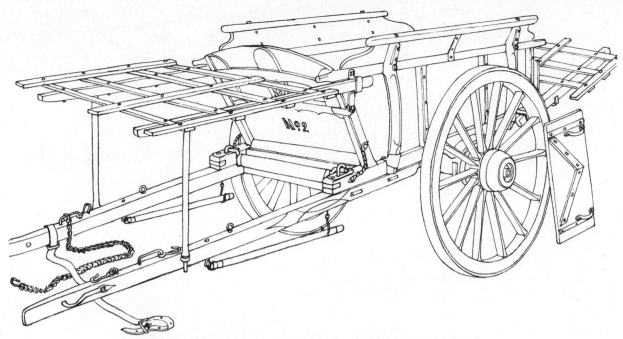

97 North-East Hertfordshire: Made by Bysouth of Braughing. Body blue; wheels, shafts and ladder orange. Body locked by strap-stick

98 Mid-Buckinghamshire: Built by Capp of Stewkley, near Leighton Buzzard. Body Saxe blue, wheels, shafts and ladder salmon. Body locked by strap-stick

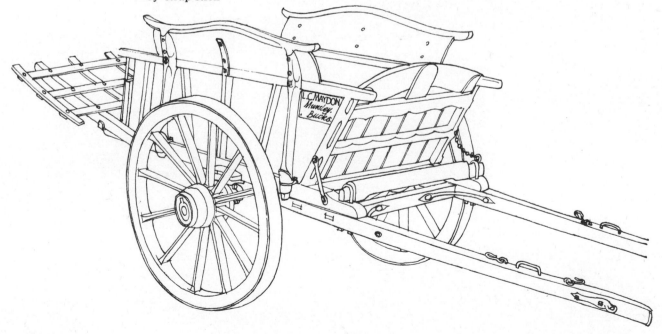

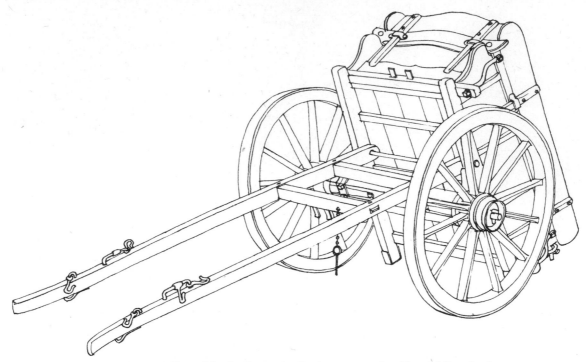

99 Wester Ross (North Strome): Entire cart red with viridian body frame. (Tipping-gear incomplete).

100 Carmarthenshire: From Cil-y-cwm near Llandovery. Body royal blue, wheels and shafts red oxide. Body secured by spring sword and sliding ring

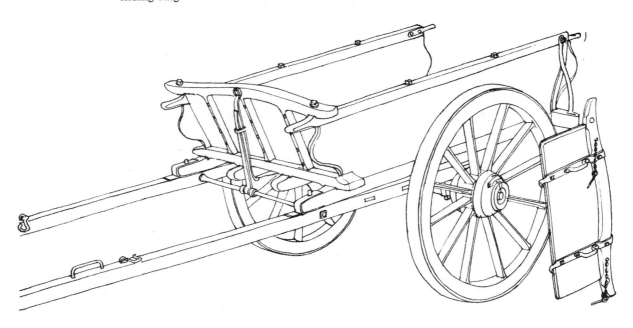

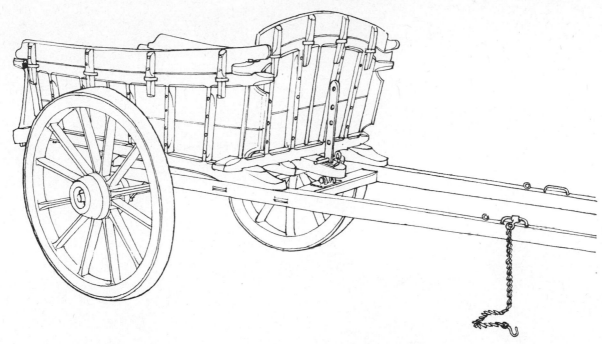

that were a little larger, had fixed boards and even carried ladders. It is clear that the use of the term 'Scotch' was confined to the eastern half, especially East Anglia, where such terms as 'box-cart' and 'butt-cart' were unknown. The two designs of cart may be summarised:

EASTERN	WESTERN
Usually large and often multi-purpose	Usually smaller and single-purpose
Large ladders fore and aft	No ladders, or only small fore-ladders
Fore-ladders extended over shafts	
Permanent side boards	Removable side-boards
Shafts hinged to body	Body hinged to axle-bed
Body bolted to axle-bed	Axle-bed bolted to shafts
Strap-stick lock	Sword lock

There were variants and hybrids to confuse matters, having features not common. Examples were noted in Wester Ross, Derbyshire, Worcestershire, Gloucestershire and elsewhere. Just as the name Milford was associated with Devon, or Weller with Sussex, so that of Bysouth was with Hertfordshire. Mr Bysouth was still making

101 **Montgomeryshire:** Built at Bettws Cedewain, near Newtown. Entire cart red, with blue body frame. Body locked with sword and peg

carts in the late 1940s at Braughing in the north-east of the county (see Fig 97). (Braughing is pronounced Braffing.) He was making two sizes of tip-cart, the smaller of which had taken prizes at recent shows. It was rather shallower than most and had a straight, planked body, without ribs, that was locked in place by the strap-stick. This was a simple device, a kind of eccentric roller that held itself in place until it was lifted and moved sideways. The hind-ends of the body frame were extended to form bumpers for contact with the ground when the body was tipped. The tail-board had no hinges, but dropped into slots making it removable. The cart ran on 4in hooped wheels with twelve spokes.

The larger Bysouth cart appeared to be the prototype of that commonly to be found in the region between Ely, Hitchin, Leighton Buzzard and Buckingham, with only detail variation. The quite deep body had a straight sheer rising to the fore with a sloping head. The sides were strengthened by spars and supported at the hind-end by iron standards. The fixed boards were set at a steep angle outwards, and the extended fore-ladder was typical and supported by a pair of sticks. Beneath each shaft-blade there was the usual toe-stick which could be let down to take the weight when standing. The tail-board was of the slot type. The large cart had fourteen spokes in 4in wheels.

123

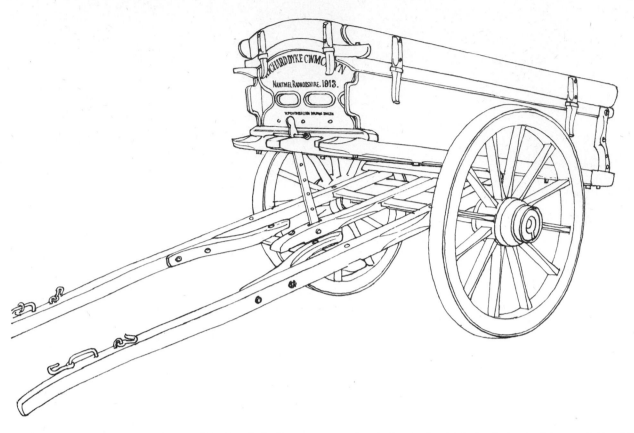

102 **Radnorshire:** Built by W. Prothero & Son, Builth, in 1913. Body buff, wheels and shafts salmon. Body locked by sword and pin. Note the incised lettering, the large (52in) wheels and the staggered spokes

While most of these carts were blue with red wheels and shafts, one, branded 'Snow, Much Hadham', had orange wheels. A small Bysouth was noted at Farnham near Bishop's Stortford owned by F. M. Prime of Walker's Farm. It had a green body with red wheels.

The carts made in North Buckinghamshire had a slightly different pattern of strap-stick but their bodies were similar. The wheels had only twelve spokes with treads of from 3in to 4in. One cart, noted near Leighton Buzzard, was branded 'L. C. Maydon, Mursley, Bucks' and had been made by Capp of Stewkley in the neighbourhood (see Fig 98). With all the features of the large eastern cart, it had a Saxe blue body with orange wheels. In northern Essex one found carts which did entirely conform. One of them, made by Whitlock Brothers of Yeldham, had a lever-operated sword that gave five positions of tipping angle. The planked out-raves were set rather flatly, like those of most waggons (see Fig 95). At Cressing, near Braintree, I found four identical

carts in their shed which had six positions of tip. Farther east, in the Southminster district, all the carts seen conformed to the eastern type.

The large tip-cart was also noted in Bedfordshire. One such cart, branded 'Messrs S. M. Browne, Sharpenhoe' (north of Luton), carried the large supported ladder and a head-board with the curious 'spectacle' motif that was common to many vehicles in the Ouse valley. Much the same design prevailed in the Holland part of Lincolnshire and in Kesteven, but these had the boards still more flatly projecting. The majority had the ubiquitous 4in wheels, but a few, no doubt made for the soft fenland, had 6in wheels shod with hoops. The carts made by Bingham were well constructed and beautifully finished. The head-boards were elaborately painted and the whole cart very well lined out. They had a lever lock, different from either strap-stick or sword (see Fig 96). At the time I was there, in 1948, James Ruane, who farmed Rising Lodge near King's Lynn, owned fourteen carts and a number of waggons. Tip-carts and waggons appeared to enjoy equal status and treatment in Holland.

In Lancashire, where waggons were not known to have been

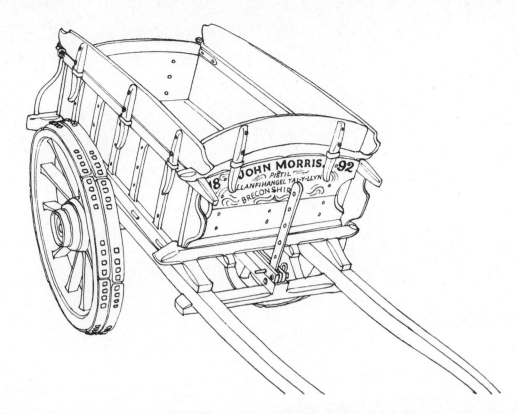

made, there were at least two designs of tip-cart; a Butt-cart and a Moss-cart. The Butt-cart was rather shallow but deeper forward than aft, and was locked by a strap-stick. The 4in wheels with twelve spokes were hung on axle-trees. The body was blue and the wheels and shafts red.   This cart was commonly used in Bowland and the Lune valley (see Fig 107).

The Moss-cart was quite small and was designed to work on the soft ground of the moss, between Manchester and Liverpool. It had 6in wheels tyred with hoops with twelve spokes and the particular example noted had iron axle-arms. The body was hinged to the axle-bed and secured by a V-clip alone. One Moss-cart, noted at Chilcheth near Chat Moss (of railway history) was branded 'Herbert Scout, Farmer, Chilcheth'. It had a red body but the shafts and wheels were white (see Fig 106). In the West of England the tip-cart of the Exe valley was also called a Butt. It was rather small, constructed in the western manner, and could be deepened by the addition of boards (see Fig 105). Most western carts had a gentle sheer to the sides which the eastern carts lacked, being straight. This sheer was to be noted as far east as Farnham in Surrey. The Exe Valley Butt ran on 3in wheels with a diameter of

103 **Breconshire:** Built at Talgarth. Body blue, with white name-board, date red. Wheels and shafts salmon. Body locked by sword and pin

no more than 36in, which set the body much nearer the ground. One particular cart had a slightly concave floor fore and aft, frequently to be noted on some of the Wiltshire carts.

Still in the West, Bristol Wagon and Carriage Works made a variety of designs to suit regional practice. An agricultural cart made by them clearly shows the influence of Wiltshire and Gloucester in the easy curves. Even the shafts, seen in elevation, had a very slight cyma curve. The panelled body also had a sheer to the profile and the almost inevitable cow-horn head supported with plank raves, with a Y-standard at the hind-end. The body was locked by a sword. The design was made in two sizes, one to carry 20cwt on 2½in wheels and a larger to carry 30cwt on 3½in wheels. A larger cart, called a Bedford, had much straighter lines with an elaborately constructed head, which, however, lacked the spectacles. Large ladders, extended fore and aft, were supplied and as usual the design was available for 25cwt on 2½in wheels or 40cwt on 4½in wheels. Yet another design, called a Yorkshire, had an elaborately constructed head after the Yorkshire manner and

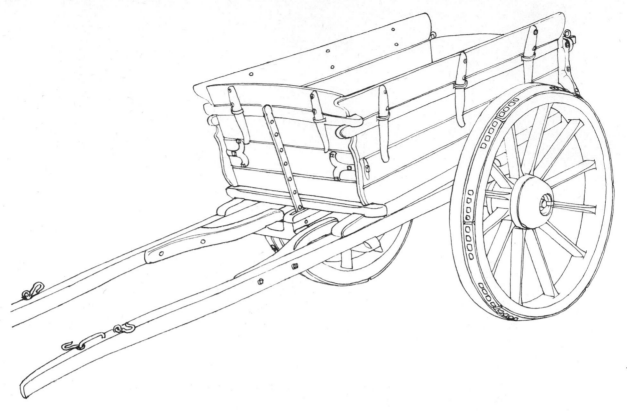

104 **Herefordshire:** Built by Geo. Palmer & Son, Leominster, in 1930. Body blue with white grooves. Wheels and shafts red. Body locked by sword and pin. Note broad wheels with strakes and hoops

again was available in two sizes, the smaller to carry 15cwt on 2in wheels, and a larger for 25cwt on 3in wheels, thus indicating the smaller all-round dimensions of all Yorkshire vehicles (see Fig 110). All the Bristol waggons and carts were available with oil-axles as required.

David Wray made a diagram of a Derbyshire cart in 1949. It was eastern in type but had a tail-board which slid sideways into position and was locked on the left hand by a curious system of levers. The 4in wheels were unusually large at 56in (see Fig 108). Among the eastern carts, those made in Kent had some resemblance to those made north of the Thames, having steeply set fixed boards and large ladders. In other details they followed Kentish practice.

Carts built by Sturt at Farnham had a tip-lock similar to the Kents but the easy sheer hinted at a western orientation but with the eastern structure. In the Marches, west of the Malverns, there was some diversity, though all the carts followed western practice with the sword lock. Detachable boards were fitted and had the same long, well-chamfered pegs as on the waggon boards. While many had slotted tail-boards, not a few had either barred or pin and eye hinges. Jones of Hereford made carts with 4in wheels

105 **Devon Butt-Cart:** Built by Newton of West Knowle, Dulverton, in 1921. Body blue. Wheels and shafts red? Body locked by chain

106 **Lancashire Moss-Cart:** Body and wheels red. Shafts white. Note 6in hoops. Chilcheth is near Chat Moss

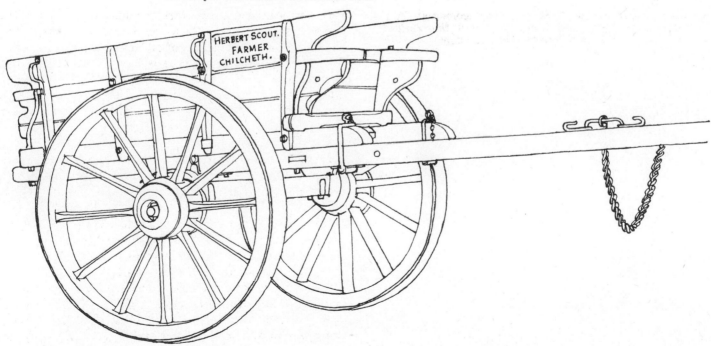

HERBERT SCOUT.
FARMER
CHILCHETH.

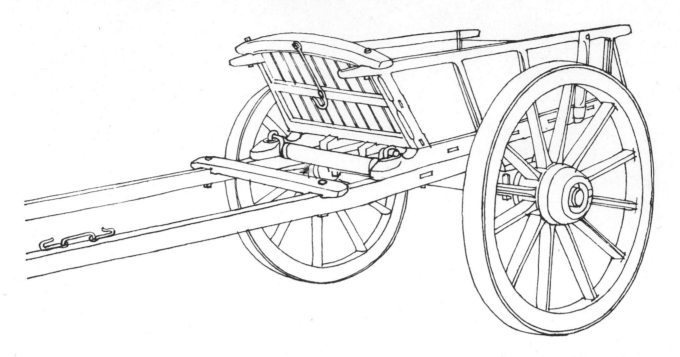

107 **Lancashire Butt-Cart** (Bowland and Lune Valley): Body blue, wheels and shafts red. Body locked by strap-stick. Large wheels on wooden axle-tree. 4½in hoops

108 **Derbyshire:** Built by Bond of Mackworth. Body buff, wheels and shafts red. Body locked by strap-stick. Shafts hinged to axle-bed. Large (56in) wheels

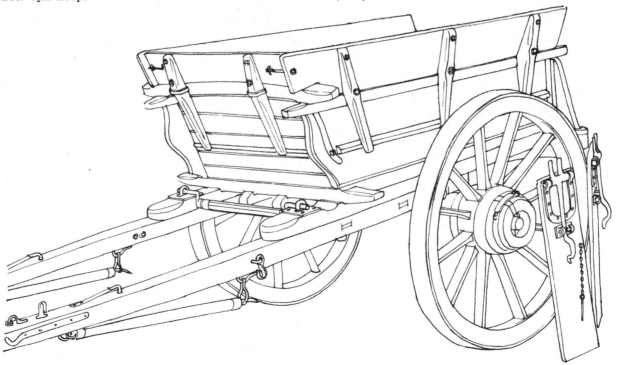

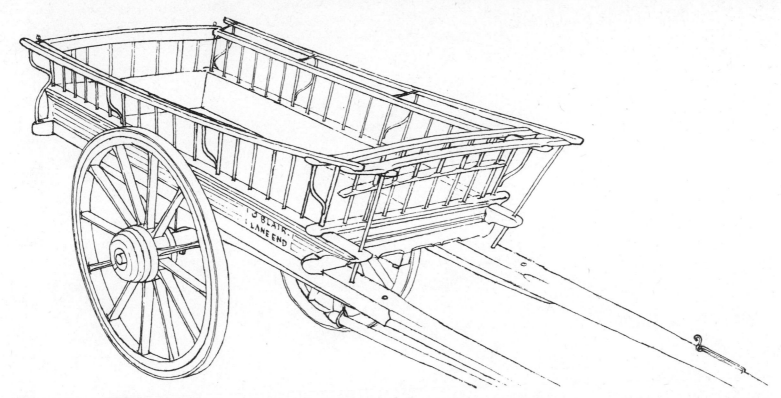

having a diameter of 48in and Williams of Pudleston, Hawkins of Thornbury and Fawkes of Brimfield likewise built to 4in. But many carts in the southern part, westward to Brecon, had straked broad wheels. Opinions on relative merits appear to have been divided, but many men asserted that the broad wheel held its ground better in the worst conditions of soil and gradient.

Among the various designs in the Marches, there were those with heavily panelled bodies and others with planked bodies. They usually had the coloured grooves common to the waggons. This was the only decoration. Evans of Kings Caple made a handy little cart called a Dobbin, the body of which was hardly more than 12in deep. It was very useful for the odd job.

In Wales Prothero & Son of Builth made carts which were wholly western in type. They had distinctive head-boards on which the lettering, faultless in execution and style, was deeply incised. The date of make was also incised. This branding was on a well-shaped panel. At Bettws Cedewain, north of Newtown, a well-made cart was noted. It had an easy sheer to the body and the usual sword lock. The 4in hooped wheels had a diameter of 48in. The cart was finished in red with the framework in viridian and red wheels and shafts, a departure from the salmon-orange usual to Welsh carts (see Fig 101). North of Llandovery, near Cil-y-cwm,

an interesting cart was noted. It had 3½in wheels tyred with hoops. Both the head- and tail-boards were set at a rake, the latter having pin and eye hinges instead of slots. The colours were a blue that was more cobalt than Prussian, and the usual deep salmon for wheels and shafts. A very fine cart was recorded near Talgarth where it was probably built. It was standing next to a broad-wheeled waggon clearly made by the same wheelwright. The cart was branded 'John Morris' and the waggon 'C. M. Morris', both of Pistil Farm, Llanfihangel-tal-y-llyn, Breconshire, and the cart was dated 1892 while the waggon was undated. Both had panelled bodies and the cart had boards all round. The head panels were ornamental, painted white, and to be found on any cart or waggon between Brecon and Kington. The body was Prussian blue and the wheels and shafts salmon. The tail-board was hinged pin and eye (see Fig 103).

J. M. Jones of Maes-y-wern, Machynlleth, has a collection of Welsh carts and waggons, including a Trumbel or tip-cart which he has restored. It has a panel-sided body with five deep spars along the sides and four on the head. The sides have a marked

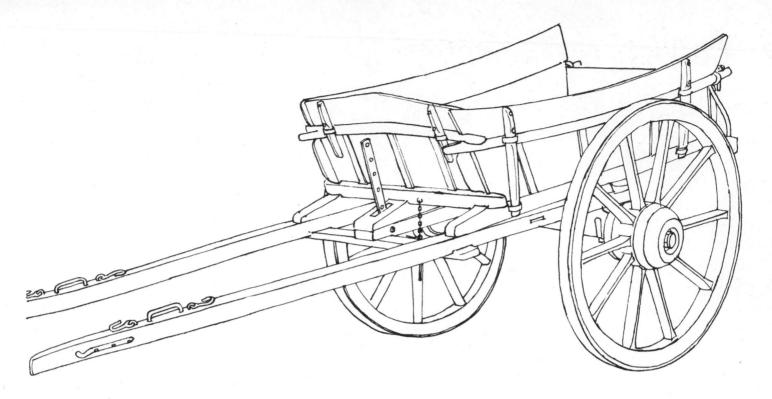

110 **'Yorkshire' Cart:** Built by Bristol Wagon and Carriage Works Ltd, c1905. Colours to choice. 15cwt body on 2in wheels or 25cwt body on 3in wheels. Oil-axles to choice

forward sheer and the head has a convex rail, but was not fitted to take boards when it was built some 200 years ago. This makes the cart a very important acquisition and as one might expect the floor is long-boarded while the wheels run on axle-trees. The lock is of the sword type and the cart is wholly western. The 4in wheels have been retyred with hoops. The body could be removed for timber haulage.

It has been stated that except for gambos and wheelcars, carts were not equipped with chain brakes, but in Wales it was customary to use a sledge, trailed behind as a brake. It is a matter of surprise that the tip-cart came late to Wales, where various hand-carriers, sleds, and then the gambo, were all well established. It may be noted that all tip-carts made expressly for manuring etc were fitted with long-boards to give a clean discharge and it was usual to set the tail end of the body wider than the head by a couple of inches.

7 Harvest-carts, Gambos, Long-carts and Wheelcars

Unlike the familiar tip-cart, the harvest-cart and the long-cart had fixed bodies. Gambos and wheelcars had no bodies but a kind of platform with side frames. All four types were low-loading and extremely handy in use where the load was comparatively light. Terms can be misleading, so that we have to remember that all four types were used at harvest.

Harvest-carts

These carts varied appreciably and in one form or another were in use in various parts of the country. It follows that in lowland farming they took second place to the waggons, but they were of prime use on many farms in hilly country. In *The Book of the Farm* (vol III, 1876 edition) by Henry Stephens, there is an illustration of one which could not have been later than the book, but around the turn of the present century Bristol Wagon and Carriage Works were making an identical cart, designed to carry 30cwt on 3in or 4in wheels. They also made a smaller version called a 'Scotch farmer's cart'. The body of the larger cart was about 120in long by 40in wide. The sides curved up from the fore-end, rose in an arc above the wheels and descended to the hind-end with minimum rave heights of about 6in. Along each side there were some twenty spindles with panel-boards behind of *uniform* depth. The support was quite substantial, with short iron standards, wooden staves and a cow-horn head-rail. The floor was not more than about 32in off the ground. The cart had a removable tail-board and large ladders fore and aft. Both shaft blades were fitted with toe sticks to be let down to take the weight of a standing cart.

Much simpler versions of this cart were noted in various parts of southern England. A particularly graceful cart, made by Clanville of Pyrton, near Watlington, Oxfordshire, was noted at Bromsden Farm, not far from Henley-on-Thames. It was inscribed on the near-side frame 'R. Fleming Esq. Nettlebed' and ran on 2½in hooped wheels, 36in in diameter with twelve spokes. The cross-rails at head and tail were bolted directly on the frame, which was continuous with the shafts, and the cross-board floor was laid directly on the same members. The sides projected to rise and fall over the wheels. They were closed by short panels at each end, but were open over the wheels. No ladders had been fitted but there were a number of swivelling rope hooks. The shafts were fitted with toe-sticks. This cart, like the waggons in this region, was yellow and red and in general appearance was an obvious cousin to its bigger relative, the Oxford. Clanville made everything from hay forks to waggons and I was pleased to find a hay fork, made from one piece of wych elm, lying with the cart.

At Kelmscott, quite close to the little church where William Morris lies, a harvest-cart was recorded in 1948 in company with a yellow-bodied Wiltshire waggon branded 'Eavis, Kelmscott'. It had more severe lines than the Clanville cart and the sides had a minimum depth of 3in. The raves rose over the wheels in the same manner and like the Clanville it had neither head- nor tail-boards, but there were fairly large and steeply set ladders fore and aft. The wheels were rather larger and had 3½in treads. There were toe-sticks to the shafts. Like the Clanville cart, this one at Kelmscott was yellow and red and had recently been painted. I made

131

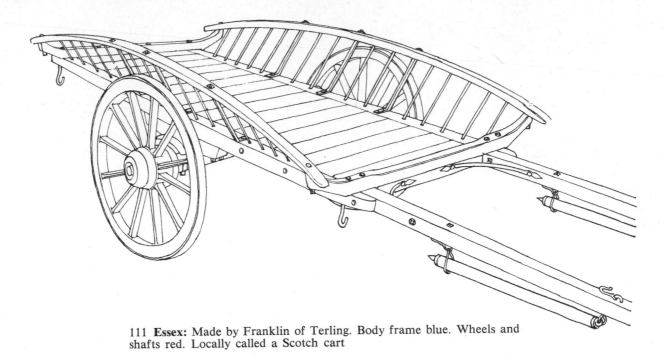

111 **Essex:** Made by Franklin of Terling. Body frame blue. Wheels and shafts red. Locally called a Scotch cart

112 **South Oxfordshire:** Made by Clanville of Pyrton, near Watlington. A very late version of the cart devised by Henry Hannam, a Dorchester farmer, in 1832. Body frame yellow, wheels and shafts red. (The hayfork was made of wych elm)

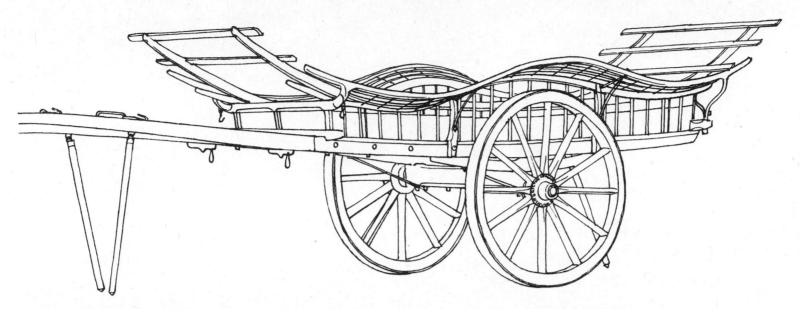

113 **Harvest Cart:** Made by Bristol Wagon and Carriage Works Ltd. A development from the Hannam cart (*Fig 112*). Bristol also made a smaller version, called a 'Scotch Farmers' Cart'. The larger cart carried 30cwt on 3in or 4in wheels

114 **Devon Curry- or Kerry-Cart:** Built by Page of Dulverton in 1917. Body and shafts blue, wheels and ladders red

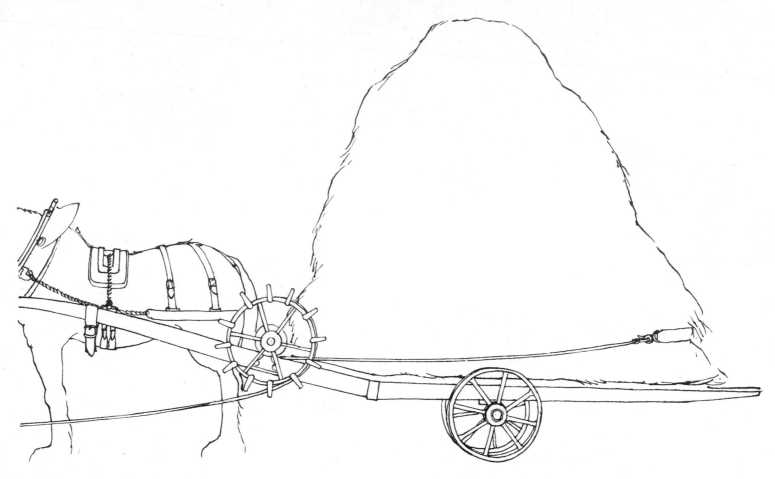

115 Hay Sledge (Scottish Lowlands): First made in the 1880s by John Wallace & Son, of Glasgow

some inquiries here but all I could gather was that such a cart was locally called a Scotch cart!

Franklin, a wheelwright at Terling, near Witham in Essex, made his own version which had a longer floor and ran on wheels of 54in diameter, with 3in treads. The raves were set in a constant shallow arc from front to back in both elevation and plan, since they began and ended at the side frames. Each bow was supported by three iron stays with fourteen spindles. They were left open, without any panelling. Each iron stay projected at about 45° from the side frames. There were large, fixed rope hooks that resembled meat hooks, fitted at the corners, but no ladders were present. The usual toe-sticks were fitted. This cart was painted blue and red and, unlike the other harvest-carts, was not locally known as a Scotch cart since the region abounded in the large tip-carts of Scotch type.

In the Dulverton district at the head of the Exe valley, a Curry- or Kerry-cart was used. One such cart, made by Page of Dulverton in 1917, has been recovered by Ralph Alford for the museum at Tiverton. The Curry, although a harvest-cart, differed from the others in having a deeper body of uniform depth, which was built more like a waggon. With the side frames set like all fixed-bodied carts, directly on the axle-bed, the Curry was a low-loading cart. It had mid-raves, projecting out-raves with fourteen spindles on each side, and panel-boards along the lower half. The head and tail were similar but without boards. The ladders and front and back were set steeply. The cart ran on 2½in wheels with diameters of about 42in, flatly dished. The shafts were without toe-sticks.

Phillips of Bridgetown near Dulverton built a flat cart, locally called a Long-cart, bearing no resemblance on any point to the long-cart used in Wales. It was quite primitive in design and had straight projecting rails. The floor was set higher than usual and ladders were fitted fore and aft.

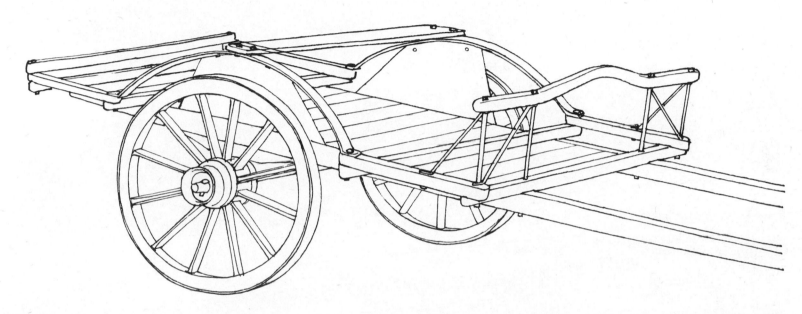

Gambos

In almost every part of Wales and intruding into the English Marches, the Gambo was, and here and there still is, in general use for harvest work and general purposes. It is the simplest of all the carts, consisting of little more than a long floor on members usually continuous with the shafts and low-built on medium-sized wheels. Measurements vary about a length of 96in and a width of 40in. Behind each wheel there is a vertical frame, called a stile, to keep the load clear of the wheels.

The majority are essentially similar, varying only in the structure of the stiles and the arrangement of the summers. Many have a single member parallel with the sides, but a fair number have two, arranged diagonally, joining the shafts in front of the floor and meeting at the hind-end. The axle-bed (or axle-tree in early gambos) is bolted directly to the frame, but it was by the stiles that distinction was made.

Gambos in Carmarthenshire and Radnorshire had stiles, each

116 Fifeshire: Corn and hay cart. Devised by R. Robertson in 1839. Note the arched rail

with two posts with three equidistant rails tenoned with the distance between floor and lowest rail varying. Those made in Breconshire and western Herefordshire had two rails tenoned, but some had the lower rail set high enough to clear two full-length boards, which were detachable. Gambos in the region west of Llandovery—Lampeter were of two types. One had two middle tenoned rails and a flat capping rail, but the second had one tenoned rail high enough to clear panel-boards permanently attached to sides and head, with a removable tail-board. The sides were supported additionally by iron standards on the end cross-pieces. All gambos had robust cross-pieces at head and tail, projecting, to carry the four corner poles in oblong slots. Rope rings were attached to the frames. The stiles were usually 36in long by 26in high.

While most Gambos had cross-board floors, a fine example at

135

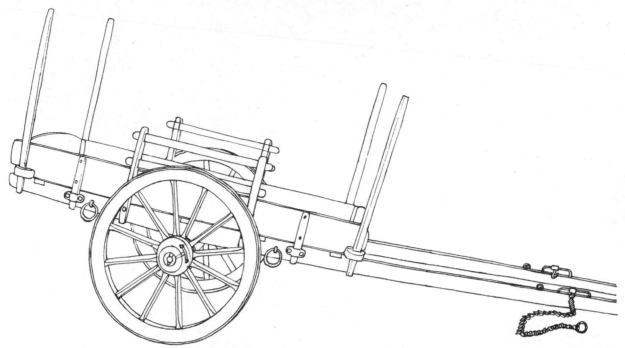

117 **Breconshire:** Aber Farm, Clydach, Tal-y-bont, where built. Body blue, wheels and shafts salmon. Iron axle-arms. Long-board floor, removable side-boards. Gambos made at Sennybridge were similar, but their wheels had ten spokes. Both had wheels 47in or 48in x 2¼in or 2½in

118 **Cardiganshire:** Llandewi-brefi and Llangeitho. Entire gambo painted salmon. Long-board floor, clear floor-space. 48in x 3in wheels on wooden axle-trees

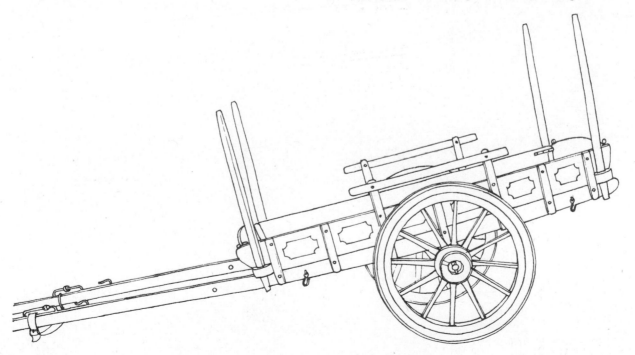

119 Carmarthenshire: Made at Caio, near the Cothi. Noted at Cwrt-y-cadno. Body blue or buff with white grooves and red wheels, 48in x 2½in. Two transverses break floor-space. Wooden axle-tree. Note the unusually elaborate construction

120 Glamorganshire: Made by James of Llantrisant. Body and shafts blue, lined white. Wheels salmon, lined blue. Clear floor-space, no transverses. Wheels 43in x 3½in, with van naves on iron arms. Note that the depth of boards tapers from 8¾in to 7½in

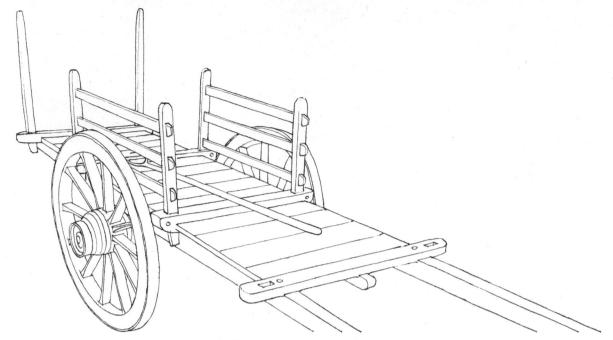

121 **Radnorshire:** Built by W. Prothero & Sons, of Builth, for Richard
Dyke of Cwm Celyn, Nantmel. Body frames buff, wheels and shafts
salmon. Wheels 52in x 3in, with staggered spokes

122 **Devon Ladder-Cart:** Lynton. Body-frame and shafts blue, wheels
red. An Exmoor counterpart of the Welsh gambo

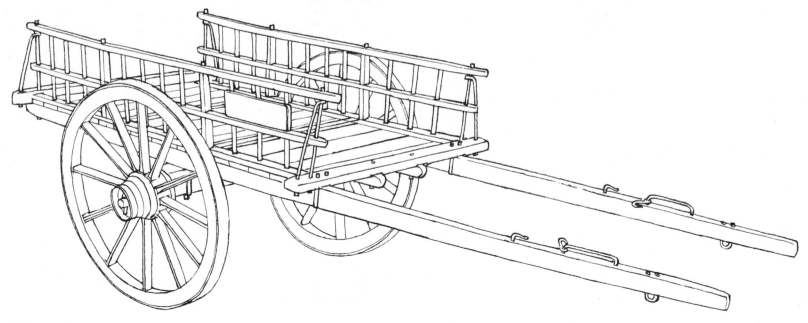

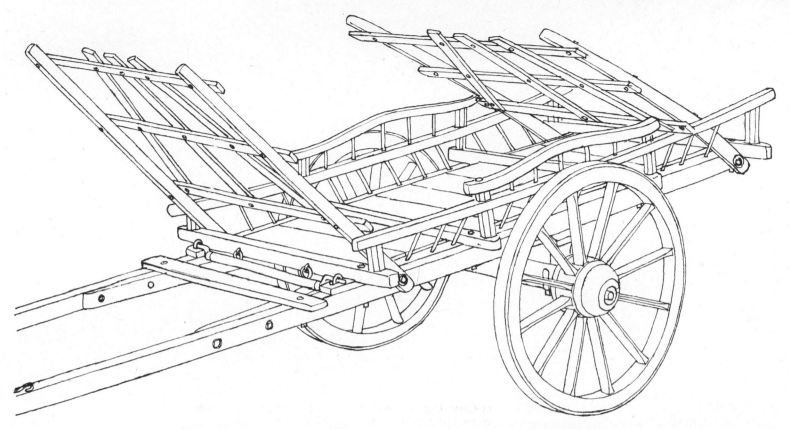

Aberclydach near Tal-y-bont, Breconshire, had long-boards and also had detachable side-boards, 13in deep. The side frames, continuous with the shafts, had a maximum depth of 5in above the axle-bed, tapering thence to fore and aft. This Gambo ran on 2¼in straked wheels, 47in in diameter with twelve spokes, dished flatly. The colours were blue and orange (see Fig 117).

A similar Gambo, built at Sennybridge, was noted at Middleton-on-the-Hill, north-east of Leominster, in company with a waggon from Corvedale, Shropshire, and another from Devon made by Milford of Thorverton. Yet another, this without boards, was noted at Crûg-y-bar, near Llanwrda, near Llandovery, it was built at Caio. Others, without boards, were noted at Llanddewr-brefi and at Cartmel. At Llwydiarth, not far from Vyrnwy, one had been made by the farmer who had a pair of wheels and an axle-bed.

Charles Martell, of Bromsberrow in Gloucestershire, has one that was made by James of Llantrisant, Glamorgan. Martell was full of praise for a most handy cart and told me how exacting James was in setting the corner poles. On too many carts one found rough lengths of ash or pine projecting unhappily (see Fig 120).

123 **Devon Wain:** Made at Blackawton near Dartmouth in the early 1890s. Preserved by P. J. Mortimore of Moreleigh, Halwell, near Totnes. Note hinged ladders (hind one folded) and strap-stick lock for tipping body, almost unique in the West Country

Long-carts

While some designs of harvest-cart were wide enough to have the frames outside the shafts, Long-carts had rather narrow bodies with frames and shafts continuous. They had shorter bodies just deep enough to clear the wheels, with the sides partly open. They were quite robustly constructed, being used on the lower hill farms in Scotland, northern England and Wales, where they were numerous west of the Cothi valley in Carmarthenshire, and in Cardiganshire about the Teifi and north to Aberaeron.

Talog is a little village near the Afon Cywyn and some three miles west of Cynwyl Elfed, near Carmarthen. A wheelwright there made a long-cart for a farmer at Llandarog, six miles east of Carmarthen. John Thompson prepared a 1:8 diagram of this cart which has a floor measurement of 96in by 48in, running on 2¾in wheels, 53in in diameter and set on a track of 54in. The axle centre is about 10in behind the centre of the body. The body,

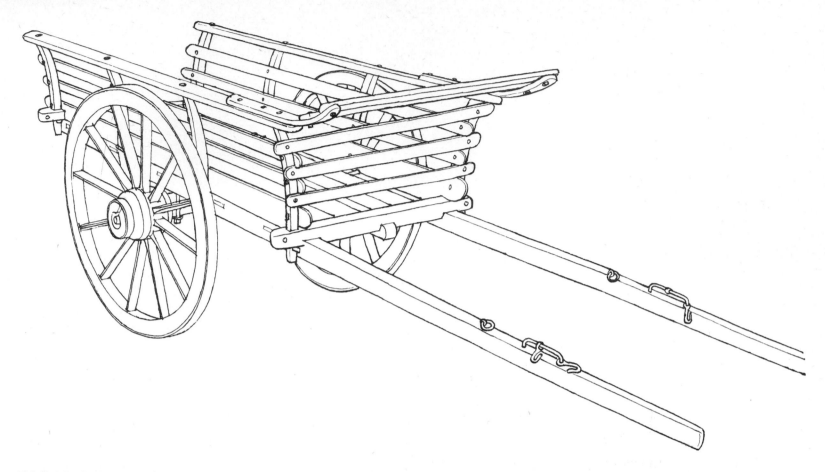

124 **Pembrokeshire:** Made at Cilgerran. Body deep buff, wheels and shafts salmon. No tail-board. Long-board floor. Forward ladder. Wheels 50in x 2½in

supported each side by four stout staves, has panels 16in deep with two rails above. The head- and tail-boards, of corresponding depth to the panels, are braced with spars, and the tail pins are fitted into brackets and are pegged in place.

A feature in the structure that makes the Welsh long-cart readily identifiable is the shape of the side in end elevation. Instead of being straight and vertical it is noticeably concave, making the width over 5in or 6in more at the top than at floor. The Talog cart is at the Welsh Folk Museum, St Fagans, together with another that was built in 1915 by Davies of Sarnau, which lies between Cardigan and Aberaeron, for John Griffiths, also of Sarnau. This Sarnau cart is similar to the Talog cart, but has a plain head and tail. The body is 98½in long by 53in over at top and running on 2½in wheels, 58in in diameter. A third long-cart at St Fagans came from Sennybridge, miles away and between Llan-

dovery and Brecon. This one was 90in long by 50in over and ran on 2¾in wheels only 50in in diameter. This cart carried ladders.

Down beside the lower Teifi a more open-sided cart was noted in 1948. Generally of the same dimensions as the Sarnau cart, it had shallower panels with three rails above, with a matching head-board but no tail-board. In most carts these rails were tenoned through the uprights, but with the capping rail laid flat. This cart was noted at Cilgerran and was distinguished by a short fore-ladder permanently bolted flatly, with the extremity upcurved and extended 15in over the head (see Fig 124).

These four long-carts had different colour schemes. The Talog cart was wholly salmon-orange. The Sarnau and the Cilgerran carts had ochre bodies and salmon wheels and shafts, while the Senny-bridge cart was blue and salmon. Opinions may differ about that orange, but in Pembrokeshire, all around Fishguard, they painted all exterior wood, such as carts, ladders and field gates a rich orange that seemed redder than that of the East Midlands. In all that hilly country between St Davids and Strata Florida the

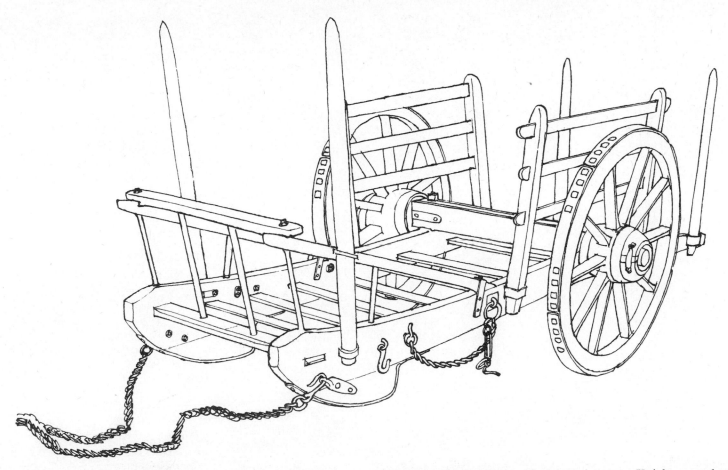

traveller may wander through little villages, whitewashed and slate-roofed, rude of exterior but rich in their interiors, and then perhaps stop in Llandyssul or Tregaron and hear no word of English. The farmer who has just come down from the hills may have come by Landrover or he may have preferred his stocky pony.

Wheelcars

As well as long-carts and gambos, various types of sleds and slide-carts, etc, have been used on the higher hill farms. Some of these were obviously of early origin, while others were of much later development. They were commonly used in Scotland, on the Pennines and in Wales and also in part of south-west England, where wheeled carts were hardly suitable. The crops of hay or oats were light enough so that with a few journeys the harvest could be gathered.

A sled had the merit that it would stay where it was left on the slopes, where the wheeled carts could be difficult to manage. Many

125 **Radnorshire:** Built at Chapel Lawn, near Knighton, and working at Obley, near Clun, in 1949. Entire wheelcar salmon. The sides were 147in long, with wheel centres 84in from the front. Wheels were 48in x 3in, straked, on a wooden axle-tree. Drop-chains both sides. Note that this wheelcar is 15in shorter than the one at St Fagans

sleds were quite elementary, consisting of no more than a platform on runners, with corner poles, and usually hauled by ox or horse. Others had rudimentary sides, which were quite open, but having vertical, close-set spindles.

From this more evolved sled, with sloping rails, the wheelcar was developed, until it had acquired the form shown in the drawing, during the nineteenth century. I found this particular one at Obley, which is up in the hills between Clun and Knighton, and it very closely resembles that which was made by Lewis at Rhos grûg, near Llanbister Road Station on the railway between Craven Arms and Llandovery. It was probably built at Chapel Lawn at the foot of the hills, some miles east of Knighton.

The wheelcar was an advanced form of sled that ran on a pair of wheels. The Obley sled had massive side pieces, 147in long, with a maximum depth of 8in at the nose tapering to 6in at the point of suspension below the axle-tree and then tapering more sharply to 3in at the tail, with a constant thickness of about 3in. A feature was the overslung axle-tree (or underslung sides), the centre line of which was 84in from the nose. A massive carriage bolt and nut held the parts together at each side. The nose was shod with sled runners and the car thus ran at all times on nose and wheels, which ran free on the level or in ascent, but were both braked with drop chains for the descent, like a broad-wheeled waggon. For this there was a set of drop chains each side with the usual 'dog and ring'. The horse was harnessed by trace chains to two large hooks on the nose.

The wheelcar had no floor planks but between each side there were six transverse keys forward of the tree and five aft with two iron rods to brace the structure. Behind the wheels there were large stiles resembling those on a gambo with three rails tenoned through two uprights each side.

At the nose end two wooden bars were supported by iron vertical rods, from which point each went down to meet the sides in front of the stiles. A head-rail joined the two with wooden spars between and standing on a robust transverse key. Iron rings were fitted to take gambo-like corner poles, with similar poles in stout brackets at the tail-end. The poles were well shaped, tapering off at the tops with their feet shaped to fit the sockets. The 3in wheels were straked and had diameters of 48in with ten spokes well dished. This car was wholly painted salmon-orange with iron parts black.

The Lewis car was larger, being 162in by 38in and the wheels were 52in in diameter on the same tread, with twelve spokes, and the frame had twelve keys.

The wheelcar appears to have been confined to a triangle of hill country between Clun, The Anchor and Pen-y-bont.

The ox was very much used in Wales and in the western half of England down to comparatively recent times. At St Fagans they have an ox-cart that resembles a long-cart, with a long draught-pole that gives a clear lead to the ancestry of the long-cart. It came from Whitland in Carmarthenshire and has a floor keyed like a wheelcar. In the same museum there is a magnificent ox-wain of the eighteenth century. The structure is very complicated and has some exquisite wrought-iron work at the head and tail. The axle and wheels are missing but one may safely assume they were of wood and straked.

Acknowledgements

My first book on this subject, *The Farm Waggons of England and Wales*, brought a response which has exceeded my most optimistic hopes. I have received some 200 letters from all kinds of people who have an active or passive interest, collectors, modellers and those ladies who, on opening the book, have 'recognised father's old waggon'.

That book was concerned solely with harvest-waggons. The scope of the present book has been extended to include all types of four- and two-wheeled farm vehicles. I am hopeful that readers who have also made long researches may be persuaded to write their own books.

To name every person who has contributed to my store of knowledge would make tedious reading, though I am none the less mindful of every one. I make special acknowledgement to R. Alford, Exeter; J. P. Bingham, Bexhill; R. C. Dobbs, Donington-on-Bain, Lincolnshire; W. H. J. Drew, Frampton Cotterell, Gloucestershire; J. G. Fowler, Acton Beauchamp, Herefordshire; Howard Frey, Penn, USA; A. Jewell, BSc, Reading; E. Jewell, Romsey, Hampshire; C. Martell, Dymock, Gloucestershire; H. Philpot, Goodrich, Michigan, USA; R. A. Salaman, Harpenden, Hertfordshire; John Thompson, Fleet, Hampshire; R. Walker, Lyminge, Kent; David Wray, Berkhamsted, Hertfordshire.

Index

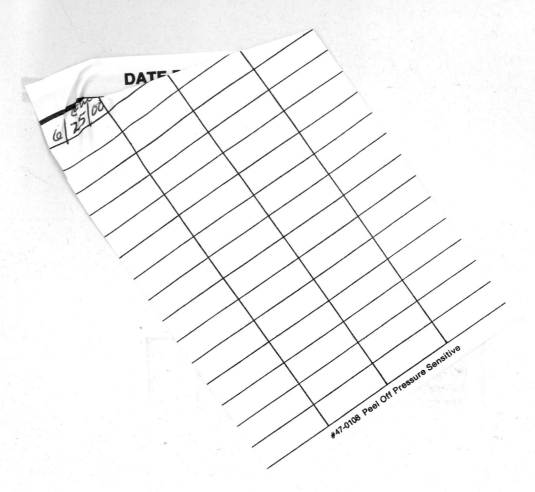
DATE

6/25/00

#47-0108 Peel Off Pressure Sensitive